A Universe
of Ethics, Morality, and Hope

A Universe
of Ethics, Morality, and Hope

Proceedings of the Second Annual
Goshen Conference on Religion and Science

George F. R. Ellis
The University of Cape Town
South Africa

Edited by:
Carl S. Helrich
Goshen College

Published by Pandora Press
Co-published with Herald Press

National Library of Canada Cataloguing in Publication

Goshen Conference on Religion and Science (2nd : 2002 :
Goshen, Ind.)
    A universe of ethics, morality, and hope : proceedings of the second annual
Goshen Conference on Religion and Science / George F.R. Ellis ; edited by Carl S.
Helrich.

Includes index.
Conference held April 12, 2002.
ISBN 1-894710-36-3
    1. Religion and science—Congresses. 2. Religion and ethics—Congresses.
I. Ellis, George Francis Rayner II. Helrich, Carl S III. Title.

BL241.G68 2003   261.5'5   C2003-902628-0

A UNIVERSE OF ETHICS, MORALITY, AND HOPE: PROCEEDINGS OF THE SECOND ANNUAL
GOSHEN CONFERENCE ON RELIGION AND SCIENCE
    Copyright©2003 by Pandora Press
    33 Kent Avenue
    Kitchener, Ontario N2G 3R2
    www.pandorapress.com
    All rights reserved

    Co-published with Herald Press
    Scottdale, Pennsylvania/Waterloo, Ontario

    International Standard Book Number: 1-894710-36-3
    Book design by Julia Stark
    Cover design by Christian Snyder

13 12 11 10 09 08 07 06 05 04 03   12 11 10 9 8 7 6 5 4 3 2 1

Table of Contents

Editor's Preface

The Goshen Conference on Religion and Science is intended to be a forum in which conference participants have an opportunity for close interaction with a thinker and scholar of international stature. The format for the conference was inspired by the very successful Cosmos and Creation conference that convenes at Loyola University of Maryland. There is a single speaker, selected as a person who is an important voice in the religion and science dialogue. The speaker presents two public lectures and one internal lecture. There are four discussion sessions. One of these follows the first public lecture and the remaining three take place in more intimate surroundings.

The first Goshen Conference hosted Professor Nancey Murphy of Fuller Theological Seminary as speaker. This second conference hosted Professor George Ellis of the University of Cape Town. Because these two speakers were co-authors of an important contribution to the science and religion dialogue,[1] the ideas expressed by both speakers were similar in nature. However, the presentations by Murphy and Ellis were quite different as were the detailed areas covered in each conference.

Professor Ellis presented the Public lectures in a style that marks a physicist. He did not read the lectures from a prepared text, but spoke them to the audience. In listening to the recordings I found that he actually spoke slowly and emphatically. But most of us found the first lecture in the chapel to be delivered at a rate that made it very difficult to follow if one were not intimately familiar with the scientific details. In speaking his ideas rather than reading them, Professor Ellis freely emphasized words and syllables of words to drive his points home. In going over the tapes it became even clearer to me how carefully he had thought through these very fundamental and complicated issues and how passionately he believed in the message he was conveying. I cannot, however, preserve the emphasis and the passion with which some of this was conveyed. Missing is the slow cadence and the almost whispered tones in which Professor Ellis asked, regarding the hierarchies of nature, "But then why do they work together so cunningly, these different forces and structures and particles, to allow this incredible hierarchical structure to exist?" This emphasis will be lost in the proceedings, as will be the chuckle that was a part of the lectures and the discussions. Lost also will be the times when Professor Ellis leaned back during the lectures and spoke without reference to notes or to the screen on which the slides were projected. It is my sincere hope that my representation of these lectures and these discussions in written form preserves the import of the ideas. Any conference has the dimension of human interaction that cannot be conveyed in the written word.

Professor Ellis brought a coherent message to this conference: there is a moral nature to the universe that reflects the kenotic nature of God and, as an integral part of that universe, our response must be consistent with that nature. The basis of this message was presented in a logical fashion and was firmly supported on the basis of the evidence. This position is almost surprising and, perhaps, radical, even to one who has spent considerable time thinking about the deeper meaning of science and of human thought.

The basic ideas on morality and ethics are not new to the theologian, biblical scholar, or sociologist, but seeking the source of these ideas and finding that in the very structure and laws of the universe is new. The issue would also remain only interesting for discussion were it not for the stature of Professor Ellis independently of any reference to his contributions to the religion and science dialog. During the twentieth century the physics community has been reluctant to make any explicit reference to metaphysics. At the same time physicists are aware of the importance of free thought and of free will. We have only been reluctant to say anything publicly about this problem. Professor Ellis was not.

There is, of course, a difference between metaphysical issues and scientific issues. Metaphysical issues cannot be decided on the basis of scientific data. Professor Ellis very clearly identified issues he considered to be metaphysical because of the impossibility of conducting experiments or obtaining data. He also discussed issues that have been ignored by hard scientists, and even considered as metaphysical because there is no evident connected causal picture. One of these is the casual effectiveness of thought and ideas. As Professor Ellis successfully argued in this conference, ideas and thoughts are causally effective, even though the physical connection may not yet be understood. This concept formed the basis for much of the discussion in the conference and is recorded here.

Another issue Professor Ellis raised was that of the intimations of transcendence. This bears directly on the question of the source of thoughts and ideas. The religious person, whether a scientist or not, will not question the reality of contact with God and of revelation. But the scientist is interested in the source of that contact, even though we may accept that a precise understanding will fail. The intimations of transcendence are evidence, or revelations of God that preserve human free will. These intimations of transcendence and the causal effectiveness of thoughts and ideas provide an indication of the area in which to seek God's direct interaction with humanity. As a past participant in the Vatican/CTNS conference on this topic,[2] Professor Ellis was also able to address some of the details of the interaction of God with humanity, although that was not necessarily the topic of the conference.

It seemed that the participants were also not quite prepared for the depth of some of this thought. With strict Quaker humility Professor Ellis outlined what he would say in simple form. What came as a surprise was the point at which we would find ourselves by Sunday morning. The object of the conference was not to convey information, although that was done. The object was to bring the participants into contact with a perspective on the universe. The universe is an embodiment of the self-giving love, the kenosis, of God. Professor Ellis is not alone in this belief, but this idea has a unique impact when presented by a respected theoretical physicist.

The basic format of these proceedings follows that of the first Goshen Conference. In the transcript of the discussions speaker numbers identify participants. Only George Ellis is identified by name. Rounded parentheses are used for parenthetical comments made by any speaker. Square parentheses are used for an explanatory word or comment added in editing. Because of the numerous references to other authors and thinkers and their publications, an effort has been made to provide footnotes to benefit the reader who may be unfamiliar with some people from particularly the scientific communities.

These proceedings include a written transcript of the teaching given in the Sunday morning worship service. A Mennonite service traditionally has a teaching by the pastor, a guest, or a member of the congregation. This is sometimes even called a sermon. In the first conference the teaching was presented by a member of the Goshen College faculty, who is an ordained Mennonite pastor, Professor Don Blosser. In 2002 this was presented by Professor Millard Lind, professor emeritus of the Associated Mennonite Biblical Seminaries. Professor Lind is an Old Testament scholar with an international stature, who has devoted considerable thought to what he presented as a teaching. The ideas there are new, but well-founded in Hebrew Scripture. It is my hope that this will add significantly to the proceedings.

It is a part of the Mennonite tradition that the teaching on Sunday morning is given, not as the word of God, but as ideas presented for discussion. This is in keeping with the Mennonite belief that church members are a priesthood of believers. Following the teaching the worship leader often asks for any responses the congregation may have. In this spirit, Millard Lind presented the teaching Sunday morning, realizing at the same time that, because of the different traditions represented, there would be no discussion at that time. So, the teaching is presented here for reflection and discussion in a broader sense.

Carl Helrich
8 February, 2003

Lectures

The principal resource for the conference is the set of lectures presented by the speaker, Professor George Ellis. There are two public lectures and one internal lecture. In addition to conference participants, the public lectures usually draw a small group of people from the Goshen and Elkhart communities. Occasionally groups from neighboring colleges have attended these as well. The public lectures are given on Friday evening and on Saturday morning. The internal lecture, traditionally intended to afford the speaker a more relaxed forum in which to express ideas, is delivered on Sunday morning. This internal lecture is presented here in edited form.

In addition to the lectures presented by the speaker, the presentation (or teaching) of the Sunday worship is also printed here. This was presented by Professor Millard Lind, professor emeritus of the Associated Mennonite Biblical Seminaries.

The principal title Professor Ellis chose for these lectures is "Physics, Metaphysics, and Meaning" with the subtitle "On Ontology and Ethics." The separate lectures are:

1. The Hidden Nature of Reality
2. Morality and Ethics
3. The Science and Religion Debate

The teaching by Professor Millard Lind from the Sunday worship service is:

4. The Bible and Evolution: The Generatings of the Heavens and the Earth when they were created.

Physics, Metaphysics, and Meaning:
On Ontology and Ethics
1. The Hidden Nature of Reality

George F. R. Ellis
7:00 pm Friday, April 12, 2002

The talk I am giving today and the talk I will be giving tomorrow are two in a series. I will cover about half the material today and half tomorrow. The title of the overall series is "Physics, Metaphysics and Meaning" with the subtitle "On Ontology and Ethics." The theme will be the significance of scientific understanding together with the importance of morality and ethics. Underlying this is the question "what is the true nature of the universe?" The underlying theme is that there is a hidden nature of reality. The nature of things simply is not obvious. It is not obvious that each of us is made of carbon, nitrogen, phosphorus, oxygen, etc. It is not obvious that I am seeing you and you are seeing me through electromagnetic waves. It is even not obvious that there is air in this room made of oxygen, nitrogen, etc. All of these basic physical facts are pretty difficult to discern and it took humankind many thousands of years before they got to understand these facts. It is not surprising if similarly any moral aspects of the nature of the universe might also be difficult to discern, and so that is one of the things I will be talking about. A part of this is also the question of which aspects are real. That will be a major theme of today's talk. In tomorrow's talk I will be particularly emphasizing the limits of certainty. That is the limits of what we can argue with certainty as opposed to what we can believe through faith.

There are two interlocking aspects of this theme. First there is the question of the way things are and the hidden nature of reality, which I have mentioned and which will be the theme for today. And then the issue of transforming the future; seeking a transforming vision of practice, which will be the theme for tomorrow. The aim is an integrated view, which is a holistic understanding entailing both a holistic vision of the way things are, and an action which tries to improve things and make life better.

So the part I am going to consider today is that dealing with the natures of existence. This will consist of reflections on causality, that is on the nature of causality, ontology, and the nature of existence. Very briefly I am going to talk about the nature of causality based on physical laws, emergent order in complex systems, top-down action undermining simple concepts of reductionism, multiple causality and complex systems and different worlds comprehending different aspects of reality all interlinked. Now that sounds a bit of a mouthful, but I will return to this at the end and I think you will see that I will be able to deal with these issues.

So when considering scientific and every day understanding there are many strands of reality. There is higher level emergent order, and we will talk a lot about that. This higher level emergent order has multiple explanations. I will be going into these, but the point I want to make at the moment is that there are two different kinds of data. There are scientific data gathered when we set up experiments under very carefully controlled conditions. We measure things with enormous accuracy, but there are also data from every day life. We are all living out every day lives and we have a great deal of experience we accumulate through those every day lives that we lead. Those every day lives are data about the universe because we live in the universe and we are made of the stuff of the universe. Data from every day life are just as much data about the universe as those carefully controlled scientific experiments. One of the questions is how do we integrate that kind of every day data with the much more controlled scientific data? We will run across the limits of scientific explanation which will lead to metaphysical issues and topics beyond proof, but that will mainly be tomorrow.

Now let's get on to the scientific view. The scientific view deals with the large, the complex and the small: in the large we deal with galaxies, stars, and planets; in the small we deal with molecules, atoms, and elementary particles; and in the complex we deal with the complex ecosystems, with societies of individual human beings and other animals, and living cells. These are in a sense the three main divisions of what science has been looking at. I am going to give a very brief summary of some of these issues. In this I am trying to paint a very large picture and for that purpose I am going to go quite rapidly through various themes. We can discuss these later on in the discussion periods.

Now the first theme is the large-scale view. The large-scale understanding we have is that the universe has expanded to its present state from a hot big bang whose physics is well understood back to the time of element information and conjectured even earlier than that. The cosmic microwave background radiation, recently examined in detail by the COBE satellite and the MAXIMA and BOOMERANG balloons, is relic radiation from the hot early phase of the universe. Now this little paragraph summarizes an enormous amount of work that has been done in the past century. But I think that every serious cosmologist believes what is in that first statement. The universe has expanded. It was very, very hot early on. In the early times in the universe there was nothing but elementary particles banging into each other. It was far too hot for any structures like atoms or molecules to exist. It cooled down and the early elements, the nuclei of the light elements, formed. It cooled down further and then the radiation and matter, which had been tightly coupled, de-coupled. Perturbations in the matter density then grew into galaxies and clusters of galaxies, which developed stars around which planets eventually formed. The radiation traveled freely from that time of decoupling and we see it today as this absolutely remarkable black body radiation. At the moment it is three degrees Kelvin. That is three degrees above absolute zero. After it was emitted at about three thousand degrees it has cooled by a factor of about a thousand because the universe has expanded by a factor of a thousand since the radiation was emitted. Typical star clusters in the present day are made up of a couple of hundred thousand stars. Star clusters are made up into galaxies. Galaxies live in clusters of galaxies. In the famous Hubble deep field, as far as we look we just see more and more galaxies. The crucial point lies not so much in the big galaxies you can see easily, but the tiny blue spots between them, which are further and further galaxies. Each of those very faint blue spots, which you can just about see in the Hubble Deep Field photos, are also galaxies in early stage of evolution. There are about ten to the eleventh galaxies. That is, there are a hundred thousand million galaxies in the observable universe. In each of those are roughly a hundred thousand

Hubble Deep Field, January 2003

million stars, each star being in the end something like our sun. And, incidentally, in all of these galaxies we are probably looking at many hundreds of millions of planets with life on them.

One of the fascinating things we have seen in recent times is gravitational lensing. In some of the images from the Hubble telescope you can see very bright massive objects around which there is a kind of circular pattern of light.

Those light arcs are in fact very, very distorted images of much, much more distant galaxies. The light has been distorted by the gravitational field of the cluster of galaxies that can be seen at the center. This is the present day version of the light bending that was so exciting in 1919. At that time the light bending predicted by Einstein was observationally verified and made the theory of relativity a headline in the *New York Times*. So this is gravitational lensing. These are very, very highly distorted, multiple images of very far objects. By measuring those images and analyzing them we can estimate the amount of mass in the lensing galaxy and this is one of the ways we estimate the mass density in the universe.

Now consider the cosmic background radiation. As I mentioned before, it is roughly 2.75 degrees Kelvin. What you see in the all-sky temperature plot is a dipole anisotropy. Tthe red spot is the hot spot, and opposite in the sky is the purplish spot, which is the cold spot. But that anisotropy is incredibly small. It is one part in a thousand of the microwave background radiation temperature. That is, the microwave background is very, very slightly hotter in one direction than the other. The reason for that, we understand, is because we are moving at three hundred kilometers a second relative to the universe. Our earth is not stationary; it is moving. Because of that motion the Microwave background looks hotter in one direction than in the other. If you remove that motion you are left with the revised anisotropy plot, which is a picture of the original background radiation fluctuations. Here the broad red band is our own galaxy, which interferes with our view of the far distant universe. So ignore that broad red band and look beyond. There you see tiny red fluctuations of hot spots, and tiny blue fluctuations of cold spots. This is when the universe was about three hundred thousand years old. That is, we are looking back to the surface of de-coupling about three hundred thousand years after the big bang. Those hot red spots will become huge clusters of galaxies and those blue spots will become huge voids between the galaxies. This is the furthest we can look back to the very, very early universe. Studying this picture and analyzing the power spectra of the fluctuations is one of the central features of present day cosmology.

Now we turn from the evolution of the universe to the historical evolution of life on earth. I will again, in a similar way as before, give one brief paragraph summarizing an incredible amount of work by many thousands of scientists. Complex life forms, including ourselves, have developed through a process of evolution over a long time from single living cells. The basic process underlying evolution is Darwinian natural selection. I am taking this for granted because there is so much evidence for it. The information resulting from this process, shaping the growth and function of all living beings, is stored in DNA according to the universal genetic code. One of the major discoveries we made in the last century, in fact it was quite an extraordinary discovery, is that each of us is digitally coded and we are constructed out of that digital coding. I am going to take this as being the basic synthesis of modern biology, as is currently understood by virtually all biologists. The original DNA model by Crick and Watson, with the famous double helix and the bases joining each other in their double pairs, is accepted and very well understood to be the basis of the genetic code. Here we have some incredibly complex molecules containing a vast amount of information.

The third feature I wanted to focus on in my summary snapshots is that what underlies all of this is our understanding of the basic laws of cause and effect. As Carl Sagan has said, this is a huge transition from the days when we used to believe in magic and witchcraft and all of that kind of thing. In summary, the fundamental forces of physics underlie chemistry and biology and underlie emergent levels of order and meaning in the hierarchy of the structure of living systems. Basic physical laws determine what happens at the microscopic level and hence underlie functions at the macroscopic levels through bottom-up causation in a given biological structure. But the higher levels in turn affect and control the processes that work at the lower levels from top-down causation. Now the latter is not so well understood so I am going to spend some time on it.

Bottom-up causation is very well understood. If I move my arm, how does my arm manage to move? Well, through electromagnetic forces. My arm is made of protons and neutrons and electrons. There are electromagnetic forces between the electrons and protons, and when you move your arm you are utilizing those forces. Basically it is moving in a manner described by Maxwell's equations. Some particles are attracting others and some are repelling others, causing my arm to move. So the microscope structure, given in terms of those microscopic particles;

electrons, protons and neutrons, and the forces between them, are what enabled my arm to move.

In this hierarchy of causation we have at the bottom particle physics underlying macrophysics, underlying chemistry, underlying biochemistry, underlying botany, zoology and physiology, which underlie psychology. That is the basic hierarchy of structure. The idea of bottom-up action is that the particle physics underlies the nature of physics. That is, the nature of the wood in this table is governed by the nature of the particles in it. The physics of those particles underlies the chemistry of matter. One of the huge successes of science in the past century was the discovery that the periodic table of chemistry could be explained from the principles of quantum mechanics. Chemistry underlies biochemistry and so on. The causation observed at each level in that hierarchy is controlled from below by the level below.

Now I want to say a little about the nature of true complexity. True complexity is not in catastrophe theory, sand piles, or in the reaction-diffusion equations. It's in truly complex systems, molecular biology, animal and human brains, language and symbolic systems, individual human behavior, social and economic systems, complex machines, that is machines with greater than a million working parts, particularly computer systems, and the biosphere made up of interactive ecosystems. I just want to say a little bit about their nature. True complexity, with the emergence of higher levels of order and meaning, occurs in modular hierarchical structures. We have seen the hierarchy. These form modular hierarchical structures which is their own viable way of building up and utilizing real complexity. This is made possible by the existence of atomic structures that allow complex bio-molecules such as RNA, DNA and proteins with their folding properties and lock and key recognition mechanisms. These atomic structures in turn underly membranes, cells including neurons, and the entire bodily fabric of the nervous system. This is the basis of life and the human brain. The way that complexity works is through hierarchy and modularity. We are made up of modules, and it's because we are made up of modules that we can understand and that the whole thing can function. These have been investigated very interestingly in the context of computing, particularly in the discussion of object-oriented programming. It is helpful to see how those principles discovered by computer scientists are embodied in physical and biological structures. I have already mentioned that they enable simultaneous top-down embodiment of action with responses based on stored information and past history.

I have already talked about the physical structure hierarchy with quarks underlying protons, underlying atoms, underlying molecules, underlying rocks, underlying planets, underlying the solar system, underlying galaxies. As regards the biological hierarchy, we have atoms underlying biological molecules, underlying cells, underlying organs, underlying organisms, underlying ecosystems. In the brain you have neurons forming neural networks and, at the top level, the cortex. The information hierarchies are a very interesting example. We can only understand complex systems because we hierarchically structure our understanding of them. For instance in your encyclopedia under animals you find mammals, under mammals you find dogs, and under dogs you find corgies and then you in your house have Joe, who is an example of all the rest of that hierarchical structure. Then there are societies and organizations. Society is hierarchically organized because it's complex and that's the only way to run it. You have the head office, which has the branch office, which has the accounting office, which has the billing section, which has the billing clerk, and so on and so on. The only reason we can deal with complexity is because we have this ability to use hierarchy which enables us to understand and interact with complex systems. And there are machines. You have a wire, which lives in a coil, which lives in a generator, which lives in an electrical system, which lives in an automobile, and so on.

I want to very briefly say that how complex structures work is again understood through these modular units with abstraction, encapsulation, and inheritance. What abstraction means is that you hide information about the details and you only interact with the environment through global variables. What does that mean? The compound objects can be named and treated as units by appropriate labeling. This leads to the power of abstract symbolism and symbolic computation. Again the efficiency and usability of modules allow us to reduce the number of variables.

In the case of a motor car, for instance, you can just talk about the engine. You don't have to say that there are pistons and cylinders and crankshafts and all that. You can just talk about the engine. That is the abstraction as you can talk about the thing as a whole. An engine from this viewpoint is something you put petrol into. You get out exhaust gases and you get out energy. You don't have to look at all the rest of the details because it is a module, which you can treat as a black box.

Inheritance is the important feature of a hierarchy, which allows an object class to inherit all the properties of its super class and to add further properties to them. For example all mammals have the same properties, and the subclass is dogs, and so on.

In these complex physical hierarchies, top-down action is when the highest level of the hierarchy causally effects what happens at the lower level in a coordinated way. And in these really complex hierarchies multiple modes of top-down action occur as well as bottom-up action. And these enable self-organization to occur. Top-down action enables the higher levels to coordinate action at the lower levels and so gives them their causal effectiveness. This is prevalent in the real physical world in biology.

No real physical or biological system is isolated. Boundary effects and structural conditions affect top-down action. So what you have are these hierarchies. If you think just of the bottom-up causation alone you get a picture in which all the action is from below to above. The micro forces in all of these hierarchies, then, determine what is happening at the higher levels. But that is not the true picture. In the true picture there is top-down causation, and that totally changes the picture. That is why there is a reality in the higher levels in the hierarchy and why they are causally effective and ontologically existent in a meaningful sense. The higher levels control the causal effect at the lower levels. For a series of examples, consider nuclear synthesis in the early universe, the writing of the genetic code, the reading of the genetic code, the effect of the mind on the body, the effect of human intentions on material objects, the quantum measurement process, and the arrow of time. I shall now consider these in detail.

In the nuclear synthesis in the early universe protons and neutrons come together through nuclear reactions to form helium, deuterium, lithium, and tritium. Now this takes place through micro processes controlled absolutely causally by the physics which happens there, but the outcome is determined by the rate at which the temperature and density drop while these interactions are taking place. And that is controlled by the rate of expansion of the universe as a whole. So the rate of expansion of the universe at the time when nuclear synthesis takes place, a long, long way back in the very early hot universe, this macro feature of the way the universe is expanding determines how much helium and deuterium is produced because that controls the environment within which those micro reactions take place.

Top-down action is central to the two main themes in molecular biology. The DNA coding in our bodies and all animals' bodies, a particular sequence of bases in the DNA, is developed through an evolutionary process which results in the adaptation of the organism to its ecological niche. This is a classic case of top-down action from the environmental details to biological microstructure through the process of adaptation. The environment, along with other causal factors, fixes the specific DNA coding. For instance, if you're a bear and you live in the polar region, some of your DNA coding tells your fur to turn white. If you are a bear that lives in the Canadian forests some of your DNA coding tells your fur to turn brown. How did those DNA codings get that way?—through evolutionary adaptation. The process of natural selection told the bear in the arctic: "look, your DNA had better tell you to turn white because that is going to make it more likely that you will survive." The process of natural selection in the forest, in effect, the environment, said to the bear: you had better turn brown or else you are not going to be so lucky to survive. And so the environment effectively acts on the animal's evolutionary process and leads into the detailed sequences of the DNA. And that is top-down action from the environment into the microstructure of the DNA in each living object.

Now, that DNA lives in each cell. When the information is read there is also top-down action. The central process in developmental biology, whereby positional information determines which genes get switched on and which do not in each cell, so determining their developmental fate is a top-down process from the developing organisms to the cell, largely based on the existence of gradients of positional indicators in the body. Without this feature, organism development in a structured way would not be possible. Each cell in our body has to know what it is to become. The cells start off identically. All the same information is contained in each of them. If the cell reads part of the DNA it will turn into nail. If it reads a different part it will turn into skin. If it reads a different part it will turn into hair. Each cell has to know, "Should I become hair or nail or skin or bone, or what should I be?" Information is fed through positional indicators ("morphogens") into the cells saying, "You are in a position where you ought to turn into hair," and to another one, "You are in a position where you ought to turn into bone," and so on. That is the functioning of the crucial cellular mechanism determining the type of each cell, which is controlled in a specific top-down way. This is another absolutely classic example of top-down action.

For the physicist, top-down action occurs in quantum measurement. In the quantum measurement process, collapse of the wave function to an Eigenstate of a chosen measurement system is controlled by the experimenter who aligns the axes of the polarization equipment, which decides which set of micro-states can result from a measurement process, and so crucially influences the possible outcomes of the interactions. For the physicist, again the arrow of time is one of the most fascinating of the examples of top-down action. One cannot tell how a macrosystem will behave in the future on the basis of only the laws of physics and the properties of the particles that make up the system, because time reversible microphysical laws allow two solutions. One is the time-reverse of the other. But only entropy-increasing solutions in one direction of time occurs at the macro level. This does not follow from the microphysical laws. It is absolutely fundamental that Microphysics is time-reversible. There is no arrow of time there, but in our lives there is absolutely a controlling arrow of time. The only current solution to the arrow-of-time problem known to physicists seems to be that there is a top-down action by the universe as a whole. Perhaps this is based on boundary conditions at the beginning of space-time that allow the one solution and disallow the other, as discussed by Roger Penrose in his book, *The Emperor's New Mind*. And so that is an absolutely fundamental feature of life that we have, an arrow of time. Time moves in only one direction. It doesn't reverse, or move backwards, and the only way we have to understand that is again by the scientific idea of top-down action.

The final example is top-down action of the mind on the body. When a human being has a plan in mind, say the proposal for a bridge to be built, and when this is implemented, an enormous number of micro-particles are moved around as a consequence of this plan and in conformity with it. Thus, in the real world the detailed microconfigurations of many objects, which electrons and protons go where, is in fact, to a major degree, determined by the macroplans which human beings have for what will happen and in the way they implement them. We have already considered this example in the moving of my arm. When I decided to move my arm, the fact that I made the decision caused electrons to flow in a controlled way, which made the arm move that way. This is an example of top-down action from the thoughts in my brain, acting through the nerve cells in the brain and then through the nervous system, so these thoughts control how those electrons flow in my fingers. That is, my brain controls how those electrons flow.

Now with this basis I can turn to my subject of ontology and causality. Given this complex structure one can ask firstly, what is real, that is, what actually exists? Here I am going to develop previous work by Popper and Eccles and by Penrose. Secondly, one can ask, "What kinds of causalities can occur in these structures?" So I am going to talk to the nature of existence, or ontology.

In order to do this I assume the existence of physical matter: atoms and molecules. I will then assign an existence to any other kind of entity that can be demonstrated to have a measurable effect on physical matter. So as atoms and molecules exist I will say we must say something else is real if I can demonstrate that it has an effect on atoms and molecules. I will clearly distinguish between ontology, that is an existence, from epistemology, that is what we can know about what exists. They should not be confused.

Whatever exists may or may not interact with our senses or measuring instruments in such a way as to clearly demonstrate its existence to us. There are selection effects when we measure and try to see what is there. A given reality can look quite different when viewed by different channels. There are many fascinating examples from astrophysics. We can view a galaxy through radio waves, through x-rays, through the optical spectrum, through ultraviolet. It looks totally different in those different wavelengths. Our own bodies look totally different if you look at them in x-rays, through infrared, through ultraviolet and so on. Some objects may not be visible at all—neutrinos for example. There are examples in cosmology. Many of you know that cosmology today is dominated by dark matter. We do not see that matter, but we can detect that it exists. Furthermore there are horizons in cosmology just like horizons on the surface of the earth. We can't see the galaxies beyond the horizon, and we never ever will see them. So the absence of images does not imply the nonexistence of objects. There are numerous galaxies in the universe we will never see. The fact that we will never see them doesn't mean they do not exist. It simply means we will not see them.

Also, what relativity has to say about this is interesting. Some people feel that relativity says anything goes in terms of knowledge. What we see is relative. Actually relativity is a very, very strict theory. Relativity shows how images and maps of a given physical reality change when you the change reference frame. An example of this is perspective: if you move from one place to another your view of a physical object will change according to the laws of perspective. Now that is really not very surprising, but that is an example of relativity. Our view of a physical object changes according to the place from which we view it, but it changes according to very strict laws, which have been known to artists for hundreds of years. Special relativity is a similar thing. I won't be able to go into that now, but, according to our relative motion, the way we see and measure objects changes, and they change in very, very specific ways. So the relativity of images does not imply that there is no underlying reality.

In concluding this diatribe about reality and relativity another aspect of scientific reality should be considered, that being the sociology of science. While the scientific process is subject to sociological forces just as is any other human activity, and while the questions scientists ask are to some extent socially determined, the answers they obtain to those questions are not. Scientific discoveries explore and clarify the nature of reality and the universe of fundamental structures underlying the physical universe. I am responding to a situation, some of you may be aware of, which has been called the "science wars." This is the debate between scientists and some people who believe that science is socially constructed. What I am saying is that the language in which science is expressed is socially constructed, and some of the questions some scientists ask are affected by social events, but the theories and the answers are not socially constructed in the sense that they are real representations of a real reality.

Now, for existence. I am going to discuss the series of worlds which exist, following on from Popper, Eccles and Penrose. World One is the world of matter and forces, which I have already discussed in quite a lot of detail. World One is hierarchically structured, as I have discussed, and is subject to cause and effect relations, and there is a reality at each level. What I want to emphasize is that when I look at this table I can treat it as a table, and it is a real table. I can treat it as made of molecules. They are real molecules. I can treat it as made of atoms. They are real atoms. The fact that it is made of atoms does not mean it is not a real table. The nature of this reality, the hierarchical structure, is not obvious, as I mentioned. It is marvelously discovered by science. This is the world of particles and objects. And here the higher levels of emergent order come into existence because of the relationships between the constituent elements.

For example, diamond and coal are made of the same carbon atoms. They are quite different because the relations between the elements are different. These relations must then be recognized as existing, as well as the material elements. The relationships are real and the elements are real. It is the existence of these relations that allows the existence of irreducible systemic properties. That is, the whole is greater than the parts. There is an interesting thing about quantum theory as regards existence. There are unresolved issues regarding the interpretation of quantum theory and ontology. Quantum entanglement implies single objects may not have their own separate properties. Rather they exist in an entangled whole. Quantum uncertainty also relates to the nature of objects, that may behave either as particles or waves depending on the circumstances. Our observations determine which nature is manifested. I am just mentioning that for the physicists. The rest of you need not worry about that. So that is World 1 – matter and forces.

World 2 is the world of consciousness. That has three parts: rationality and understanding, feelings and intentions, and social construction, such as laws. Now remember my criterion. Why do I say the world of consciousness is real? I say it is real because these are all causally efficient. I can give you examples in which each of these is real. For instance, many material objects have been constructed by human beings. Pictures of these objects are visual demonstrations of the causal efficacy of human thoughts and intentions. A jumbo jet is an example. A hydrogen bomb explosion is not only an expression of human thoughts and intentions; it also demonstrates that human emotions are causally affective. This is a visible demonstration of the emotion of hate. And the emotion of love is just as causally affective. And some people say, "But ideas are just brain states. So this is all just a physical thing. And why are you making this song and dance about it?" Well, ideas are not just brain states. They are abstract concepts that are realized as social phenomena. The same idea, a jumbo jet for example, has multiple representations in a number of media and a coding and each medium. For instance you can think of it in your brain. You can see it in a book. You can hear me talking about it. You can have a representation of a jumbo jet in computer memories. There are many different representations of the same idea and only a few of those are in brains. Many of them are not. So, in fact, an idea is an abstracted equivalence class of these language and media representations, and can be represented in many physical ways. Thus they are not physical phenomena and they have a quite different kind of existence than matter has.

So in the causal-hierarchical structure explained in our book, Nancey Murphy and I, in fact, separated out two sides, because causality is totally different on the purely physical side, from what it is on the biological side. On the biological side all of these things, intentions, causes, and laws are functioning and are causally effective. On the physical side intentions do not exist. Let me just mention the example of socially-constructed laws. Examples of socially constructed laws in this country are certain laws relating to speed limits for automobiles and certain laws relating to emissions from the exhaust of the automobiles. Now those are socially-constructed laws. Those get written into the statute books. They move from human minds into a printed representation. They then get implemented by traffic officers. And they affect the design of automobiles and therefore they have a causal efficacy in terms of changing the shape of the automobiles in which you ride. That is an example of the causal efficacy of the social construction of laws. So the biological side involves conscious choices and the physical side does not, and that is why causality is different in those two sides and that is why we separated them out.

The Third World I want to talk about is the Aristotelian World of physical and biological possibilities. This is the world of physical and biological possibility landscapes of which a subset is explored by the real world. These possibility-landscapes, which put absolute limits on what can happen, are partially explored by what exists physically. For instance there is an abstract world out there of possible animals, and only some of them have come into being through the actual process of evolution. There could easily be, let's say, mice with six legs. Well, they do not exist, because that hasn't been a place which has been reached by evolution. But, on the other hand, there are boundaries beyond which things are impossible. For instance a mouse six feet long will not function. It will collapse on its face because gravity will crush it. Also there is a world of physical possibilities. In physics if you are playing football you can throw a ball in many different directions, but each way you throw it, it will satisfy the law of momentum conservation and energy conservation. So there is a huge space of possibilities for what you can do with that football, but that space is absolutely, rigidly constricted by those laws of energy conservation, and of momentum conservation. So there is this abstract world of possibilities from which we select a subset of things which actually happen. In a certain sense this world of possibilities is more real than the world of what actually happens, with all its contingent arbitrariness – what happens could have been different. The world of possibilities is absolute. There is no arbitrariness in it. There is no freedom in it. It is absolutely rigidly constructed. Now physicists would say, "This is the world of the laws of physics." I have not expressed it that way because the nature of the laws of physics is very debatable, but the fact that these limits exist is not debatable.

I received an e-mail entitled "Perpetual Motion." The writer claimed that:

> This is probably the most important e-mail you will read within your lifetime. I have discovered a method of generating pollution-free, unlimited energy by harnessing the forces of gravity. Our economies, our governments, our lives are run by our need for energy. Those who control energy supplies control us. It is time for freedom! My invention is what I call a perpetual-motion device of the third kind. Because all such devices in the past failed, the false belief was stated that perpetual motion was an impossibility. This is simply not true, nor is it intelligent logic.

Yet again, an impossible machine. It will not function in reality. Consider the well-known print by Escher of another impossible structure: the water that always runs downhill, running in a stream, and then falls over a wheel generating energy and then keeps running downhill. It is another impossible structure.

There are rigid limits on physical behavior, which are characterized by this world of possibilities. For example, what is possible biologically is described by the physical laws underlying biology: the second law of thermodynamics, Maxwell's laws of electromagnetism, and Einstein's laws of gravitation. We know that the behavior of matter is very well described by these physical laws, but we do not know the existential nature, the ontological nature, of these laws. We don't know if they are prescriptive, that is controlling, or descriptive, that is describing. We do not know why they are so well described by mathematics, whether in some way mathematics prescribes the nature of physical laws, but we do know that there is a set of possibilities. There is a huge set of possibilities for the future, but it is a restricted set of possibilities. It is strongly restricted, and that is what I want to say is the third kind of existence. It underlies the world of actualities. The world of actualities is chosen from the possibilities, which are in this world.

The final world I want to talk about is a Platonic world ; World 4, full of mathematical reality. This is explored, not created, as Roger Penrose has explained so beautifully. It is causally affective by discovery, because we can print out what we discover. For instance consider the basic geometrical features of Pythagoras' theorem. Pythagoras worked it out, but the same theorem applies on Mars, Jupiter, and the Andromeda galaxy. Or consider the basic relationship of a circle of radius r to its area, which is pi times r squared, where pi is a universal constant. The same results will be discovered near Alpha Centuri or in the Andromeda galaxy. This is not a human invention. The way we code it is a human invention, but we are confident that the same essential results will be found everywhere in the universe. When we discover these mathematical relations, we are not inventing them, we are discovering them.

The Mandelbrot set was sitting waiting to be discovered. For thousands of years this was sitting in this abstract space, as it were, and it was only discovered when we had computers which had enough computing power that we found it. The Mandelbrot set is generated from incredibly simple equations, but you have to repeat those equations many hundreds of thousands of times to generate that pattern. So we only discovered them when we had computers, but the computer did not think them up, in some sense. The computer found they were implied by those extraordinarily simple equations. We discover mathematical features by analytical thought and logic and computation, not by physical experiment. They are of quite a different nature. Investigating physical laws is not the same as investigating mathematical laws. We can discover them sometimes by numerical experiments. But mathematical objects and operations are not physical features of the world. They do not depend for their existence on physical objects. Indeed, like logic, they seem to pre-exist the existence of matter and physics to, in some sense, present a deeper layer of reality.

So, to summarize this, there is a reality to each separate level of physical system in the physical hierarchy of structures. There is a reality to human thoughts and emotions. There is a reality to the possibility of space that determines what is and is not possible. At the lower levels of the hierarchy this is characterized by inviolable physical laws, whose ontological status is unclear. And there is a reality to logical mathematical structures which relate in an unknown way to physical laws. That summarizes the view I am putting forward.

The underlying logic for this view is that these claims are justified in terms of the effectiveness of each kind of reality in influencing the physical world. The key point is that although physicists don't usually recognize all of these realities, their causal models of the real world will be incomplete unless they include all of them. Physicists cannot explain the existence of these spectacles unless they allow a reality to the causal effectiveness of human thought. It's not just matter or information that has physical affect, it is also thoughts and emotions and therefore intentions. However, these different kinds of realities clearly have different natures, so I am claiming that they are real because they effect the physical world. But each of the four is quite different in its nature.

Given this nature of reality, what about causality? The key point about causality is that simultaneous multiple causality, interlevel as well as within each level, is always an operation on complex systems. Any attempt to characterize any partial cause as the whole, as characterized by the phrase "nothing but," is a fundamentally misleading position. Indeed this is the essence of fundamentalism. Whenever someone says "nothing but" you know they are saying, "I am looking at this part, which I like, and I'm not going to look at the whole causal scene." This is important in regard to claims that any of physics, evolution, biology, sociology, psychology or whatever are able to give total explanations of specific properties of the mind. Rather they each provide partial and incomplete explanations, and in a sense that last sentence is why I have taken you through this long and rather laborious discussion. When anybody says that sociobiology is the total explanation of the mind, you can say, "Are you taking all the causes into account? I will bet you aren't."

There are always multiple-level explanations all at the same time. There is no single explanation. So one can have top-down system explanation as well as bottom-up explanation, both being simultaneously applicable with no conflict. The example I like is why aircraft fly. Why does an aircraft fly? Now you can sit down and you can say well there is this wing and there are molecules and air pressure below, and Bernoulli's law of pressure for the air above, which lifts it up, and that is why aircraft fly. You can give this substantiated with masses of equations. Well, that is the bottom-up explanation. Let's do the top-down explanation of why aircraft fly, which Russell Ackoff gives. An aircraft flies because it was designed to fly. People spent a lot of time designing it and manufacturing it so that it would fly. And that's the top-down explanation. They are both true.

I have talked about the effect of legislation on car design. An interesting, equivalent example is the effect of rules on football. You can talk about the flight of a football. It is due to the particles, momentum conservation, energy conservation, air rushing against the football, and all the rest, and that describes why the football flies the way it does. But equally, in an actual football match, the reason the football goes where it does is because of the nature of the rules of football. If the rules were different the football would actually go to different places, because the players would take it to different places, and that is another example of top-down explanation.

One of the most interesting examples is the effect of the mind on human health. The way medicine is traditionally taught is in terms of bottom-up explanation. That is the human mind, the brain, and so on, are all controlled by all of these microparticles. If you change the chemicals, then the brain will function differently and everything will be all right. The top-down explanation is only now beginning to be understood. There is a beautiful book by Esther Sternberg called *The Balance Within: The Science Connecting Health and Emotions*, which talks about the top-down effect of the mind on the health of the human body. She locates very carefully, in a detailed argument, molecules which are responsible, enabling the mind to influence the immune system, and so enabling the mind to influence your level of health. Well of course we all know, in fact, that stress affects your health, but somehow many medical practitioners and medical schools have lost sight of that fact because they are engaged in this engineering, bottom-up, metaphor about how health works instead of taking into account the holistic top-down way that the mind actually affects our health in a very, very important way.

In particular, in all of this, the thing I want to emphasize now is that the highest level of intentions, which is ethics, is causally affective. For instance we can consider the image of a hydrogen bomb exploding. This raises the simple question: "Will hydrogen bombs explode on the earth in the future?" Well, that depends on the ethics of the people who are in control of the countries of this world, and so ethics is causally effective. As another example, consider that in many states of the United States there are execution chambers, which are physical embodiments of the laws of those states. If those states, instead, had an ethic, which said we will not take human life, then those execution chambers, those physical embodiments, would not exist. So the highest level of causation in terms of motivation is ethics, because ethics is the statement about what motivations are acceptable and which kinds of plans you will actually implement. So in terms of this causal hierarchy, ethics is there at the top and is causally effective in the real world of physics.

Physics, consciousness, and human thoughts can cause real physical effects. This is a top-down action from the mind to the physical. In a sense it is ridiculous that I should have to say this. This is so obvious to the ordinary person in the street, but somehow the scientists have lost sight of all this. At present there is no way to express this interaction in the language of physics, even though our causal schemes are manifestly incomplete if this is not taken into account. The minimum requirement to do so is to include the relevant variables in space of variables considered. That then makes these variables and their effect a part of physics. In other words a complete causal scheme for physics, in the end, is going to have some representation of human thought because if it does not it is a causally incomplete scheme.

Related to this, for the physicist there are unresolved issues regarding the nature of consciousness and quantum mechanics. We do not know how to analyze the core issues of consciousness in meaningful ways. We do not know if there is any relation of brain function to specifically quantum properties such as entanglement. There is a very interesting question: could the evolutionary processes, which led to the formation of our brains, have missed out on quantum theory? Could they have failed to discover quantum theory? I would say that is unlikely, although most neuroscientists do not want to admit this.

Finally, how does all of what I have been saying relate to fundamental physics? Fundamental physics underlies and enables all of this complexity, which I have been talking about—these top-down and bottom-up interactions, because the fundamental physics determines the natural interactions of matter. The basic questions for physicists are, "what are the aspects of fundamental physics that allow and enable this extraordinarily complex modular-hierarchical structure to exist, in which the higher levels are quite different from the lower levels?", and "what are the features of physics that allow it to come into being?" Sylvan Schweber suggests it is the fundamental feature of a renormalization group, but this is not adequate to encapsulate the whole of this complexity precisely because it is quite different at different levels. So in terms of a theory of everything (physicists have been using this phrase, "a theory of everything"), what feature of physics is the key to the existence of truly complex structures? That is a really interesting question for physicists. What, for example, allows the modular separation of subnuclear structure, nuclear structure, and atomic structure? We have these modular levels and we can talk separately about the molecules, atoms, and so on. What is it about physics that allows a separating out of these different levels of structuring from each other in such a way as to allow the development and functioning of DNA, RNA, proteins, and living cells? Whatever it is, this must claim to be the truly fundamental feature of physics. It is the foundation of the complexity we see. Is the key the general nature of quantum theory? That is, is it the uncertainty principle, superposition, entanglement, decoherence, and so on? Is it the specific nature of quantum-field theory and quantum statistics, which we already know is absolutely crucial because that underlies the stability of matter? Is it the Yang-Mills-Gauge theory, or specific potentials for interactions? Is it related to special relativity? Is the key the basic particle properties, the existence of three families of quarks, leptons and neutrinos? Or is it the basic property of the forces, the fact that there are four fundamental forces? Is it the specific masses and force-strengths or the values of specific constants?

So physicists can ask this, and it is a really interesting question: "What is it about physics which enables this incredible hierarchy of structure to exist and to function? Is it some of these or is it the combination of all?" Probably it is the combination of all of them, but then why do they work together so cunningly, these different forces and structures and particles, to allow this incredible hierarchical structure to exist?

Finally, what is ultimate reality? There is a delightful ambiguity in the concept of what is ultimately real. Is it the fundamental physics that allows this to happen? Is it these causal foundations? Or is ultimate reality the highest level of structural complexity that is achieved; the ultimate emerging structure and behavior? On the conscious side, is ultimate reality the ethical base that ultimately determines the outcome of human actions and whatever may underlie this ethical basis? Is it perhaps the metaphysical underpinning, both of cosmology and of fundamental physics, which underlies the fundamental physics? That is, is it whatever makes specific physical laws fly rather than other ones?

So in fact in terms of this hierarchical structuring, in terms of this causal structure, we need to add a metaphysical layer under physics and a metaphysical layer at the top of cosmology. The existence of physics cannot be explored in a scientific way. I will discuss this next time. It is based on an underlying metaphysics, and the same is true of cosmology. Again, I will go into this next time. There are metaphysical things about cosmology, which cannot be determined from physics, and can only be determined from a metaphysical level, that is from a level beyond that of physics. What I said I was going to talk about tonight, and I know it has been a bit technical, but absolutely crucial to what I want to say, is that once you have admitted all of these different kinds of existence, once you have seen these are necessary for physics to be causally complete, then you have loosened up from materialism to a much, much broader understanding of the nature of existence. You have got these four different kinds of existences instead of just that narrowly construed existence of particles. That sets the stage for a much broader understanding of the nature of the universe than when you have that very, very simplistic, rationalistic idea.

What I looked at was the nature of causality by some physical laws, emergent order in complex systems, how top-down action undermines simple complex reductionism, how there is multiple causality in complex systems, and how there can be different worlds. There are four different worlds comprehending different aspects of reality, and all causally interact. You cannot leave any of them out if you are going to have a proper description of the nature of existence, and that is what I was going to say tonight. Tomorrow I will go on and start relating this to the issue of ethics and meaning.

Physics, Metaphysics, and Meaning:
On Ontology and Ethics
2. Morality and Ethics

George F.R. Ellis
10:30 am, Saturday, April 13, 2002

As I said yesterday, the overall title for these two lectures is "Physics, Metaphysics, and Meaning: On Ontology and Ethics." I talked yesterday about the significance of scientific understanding. Today I will be talking about the importance of morality and ethics. In both cases the issue is the true nature of the universe.

Last night I pointed out that the nature of the universe in physical terms is hidden; so it's hardly surprising if any ethical nature it has is also hidden. The question, which will come up again today, is "Which aspects are real?" I talked about that in some depth yesterday, and today I will extend it a little farther. Today I will be particularly talking about the limits of certainty.

There are two interlocking aspects to this overall discussion. One is the way things are: "What is the hidden nature of reality?" The other is the way things should be: "How do we go about transforming the future—transforming vision and practice?" I will say a bit more about this with the overall aim of working toward an integrated holistic vision and basis for action.

Yesterday I set up the hierarchy shown in the figure below. Then at the end I put in the metaphysics you see at the bottom and at the top on the left, and I put in ethics on the top at the right. This is the branching hierarchy of causality. On the left-hand side is the natural hierarchy for non-living objects in which there is not an element of intention. On the right-hand side is that for living beings in which there is an element of intention. I made the case yesterday that, since any intention can be causally effective, it must be taken very seriously. I also made the case that ethics is the top of this causal layer because ethics is the choice of what actions are acceptable and what are not. Ethics is, therefore, the topmost causal layer which then controls the lower levels in this right-hand branch, where intention underlies causation.

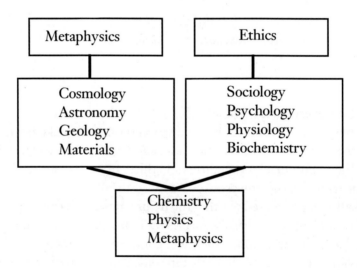

Figure 1: Hierarchical structure

Today I want to talk about what I've called the "natures of meaning" or reflections on morality and spirituality. Meaning, of course, relates to both metaphysics and ethics. I shall consider that the metaphysical option is open, but effective ethics must have an essential origin in meaning. Deep ethics is of a kenotic, or self-sacrificial, nature. I will talk about a variety of intimations of transcendence that support the idea of kenosis, and I will briefly say that in my view, true spirituality resides in an awareness of all these themes together.

I want to complete the system in terms of causal structure and in terms of associated ontology in two stages. First I want to deal with the issue of metaphysics and then I will turn to the subject of ethics. You would have heard some of this from Nancey Murphy last year because a large part of this is discussed in our book (*On the Moral Nature of the Universe* by Nancey Murphy and George Ellis(Fortress Press, 1996)).

Underlying physics and cosmology are untestable issues. Firstly is the existence and nature of the laws of physics. Physics deals in depth with the nature of those laws; it investigates what the laws are and what they predict. But physics cannot tell you why laws of physics exist. Physics cannot tell you why the laws of physics have the nature they have. Physics only investigates what the nature of the laws is. For example, physics determines that electromagnetism is governed by Maxwell's equations, but physics cannot answer the question, "Why are Maxwell's equations true?" Physics can't answer "why" because there is no related experiment. There is no experiment that can tell you "why" Maxwell's equations are true. Experiments can only tell you the nature of Maxwell's equations and how they govern electromagnetic behaviour.

Similarly, there is no experiment that can tell you "why" the initial conditions at the beginning of the universe were as they were. We can try to find out what those initial conditions were. But, we cannot say *why* they were as they were. The reason is because this was the start of the universe—we cannot go back there and do any physical experiments. We cannot re-run the universe. A further famous untestable issue is the question of why anything exists at all. We take it for granted that things exist. We cannot experimentally test why this is so.

All of these things I have listed are the starting-point, the bedrock, from which we then proceed to do physics. They are the basis on which physics exists. And physics cannot examine that bedrock; it takes that bedrock for granted.

A further very controversial, untestable issue, about which I will have more to say, is why the universe allows life to exist. This is a metaphysical issue, and the point I wish to make is that science cannot provide metaphysics. Science is built on, or takes, metaphysics for granted. Some of my colleagues do not seem to fully grasp this point, but it is fundamental.

We do know something about the conditions necessary for the existence of life. The brief statement I give here is like those summary statements I gave yesterday: *Significant alteration of either physical laws or boundary conditions at the beginning of the universe would prevent the existence of intelligent life, as we know it in the universe. If the physical laws were altered by a remarkably small amount, no evolutionary process of living beings would be possible at all. So these laws of physics appear fine-tuned to allow the existence of life.* That is the summary statement.

This can also be looked at the other way around. If the physical laws were different, or the boundary conditions were different, in most cases, life could not exist. A vast amount of writing has been done on this under the name of the Anthropic Principle. It is summarized in a big book called *The Anthropic Cosmological Principle* by John Barrow and Frank Tippler.

I will give you two examples. The first is *Limits on Physics Allowing Complex Structures* by Max Tegmark. The figure below illustrates the situation.

Along the bottom is plotted the value of something called the

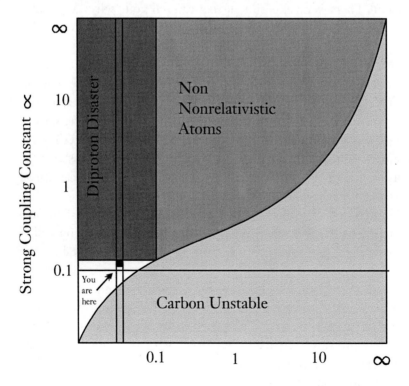

Limits on physics allowing complex structures [Max Tegmark]

electromagnetic coupling constant. Basically, this is the strength of the electromagnetic force. Along the vertical axis is plotted something called the strong coupling constant. This is basically the strength of the strong coupling force that keeps nuclei together and so enables atomic nuclei to be stable. In the light grey region, carbon would be unstable and no organic chemistry would be possible. For values of the two coupling constants in the ranges which define this light grey region, life as we know it could not exist. It couldn't exist in the medium grey region because no non-relativistic atoms could exist there. In that region there would not be any chemistry at all. In the dark grey region the diproton disaster takes place. The region which allows complex structures to form, is the small triangular region in the lower left-hand corner. The actual values of the two coupling constants place the physical universe we live in at that little black spot on the edge of the triangular region. So, if you, as a cosmologist, examine an ensemble of universes in which these two constants take different values, you will find that in virtually all of those universes there won't be living beings like us. There will be no process of evolution, no Darwinian evolution at all, because the materials of which life should be made won't exist.

Another example of the calculations of Max Tegmark is shown on page 40.

A fundamental feature of the world, as we know it, is that it has one time dimension and three spatial dimensions. Mathematically we can imagine universes in which there are different numbers of time and spatial dimensions. The dimensionality of the universe will define the sorts of equations that will describe physics in that universe. What you can see here is that if you had no time dimension you have elliptic equations and things become unpredictable, and the same is true if there is no spatial dimension and only time. So the dark grey region will not allow any complex activity to take place. If there are four or five dimensions of space and one dimension of time, things are unstable. The situation is similar for four or five time dimensions and one spatial dimension. So those regions in the diagram are no good for life to exist either. In the region for which the minimum number of either space or time dimensions is two you have ultrahyperbolic equations and so the way that signals would work is unpredictable. If the time dimensions are three and the spatial dimension is one you only get tachyons (particles that move faster than light, allowing travel into the past). In the region in which either

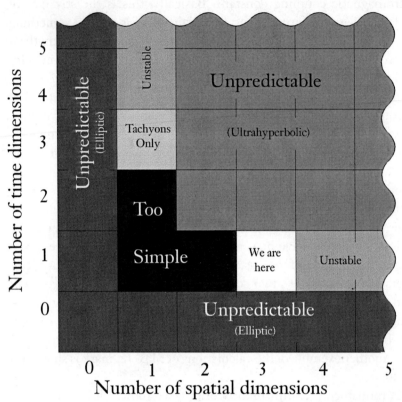

Only special dimensions allow complex systems [Max Tegmark]

the time or spatial dimension is one and the other is one or two, the dimensions are too simple for complex structures to exist. So you need one time dimension and three spatial dimensions in order to get interesting structures that can be complex enough for the hierarchies that I talked about yesterday to exist. And we live in a universe indicated by the square with a single time dimension and three spatial dimensions– as is required for interesting physics to exist.

So if you imagine again a scattering of universes with different dimensions, most of them won't allow life to exist. Only if you get the dimensions right will beings like us, or zebras, or giraffes come into existence. The question people have asked, which is a metaphysical question, is, "Why is it that the universe has those specific laws which allow us to come into being?" There are four metaphysical options. The first is *pure chance*. By "pure chance," I do not mean it is probable; I mean it just happened by chance. There is no further explanation. Things just happen to be the way they are, they are not probable, they are not improbable; that is just the way they are. That is a complete and total explanation at a certain level, but it has no explanatory power— and physicists hate that because it is just a dead end. This option simply says, "That is the way things are, there are no further questions you can ask."

The second option, which physicists like very much, is the claim that in fact *the universe is very probable*. There is a whole group of physicists who would like to say that although the universe doesn't look probable, if we understood physics better, we would be able to say that it's actually probable. Most of these ways of trying to say the universe is probable are based on thinking of an ensemble of universes. I have already mentioned this idea. So out there are many, many universes, and some things are probable in this ensemble of universes and some are not. You try to prove that existence of the one universe we happen to live in, which allows life, is probable because "all that can happen does happen" in this ensemble. My problem with this option is that it is untestable because the idea of an ensemble of universes cannot be tested.

There is a set of attempts to explain what now exists *from some previous mechanism*, and there is a vast variety of such proposals. There is something called pre-big-bang theory. There is something called the ekpyrotic universe theory, and so on, and so on. But these basically don't get us very far because unknown, untestable pre-physics underlies each of these theories. This option simply defers the question, because we then ask, "Why does that pre-physics state exist?"

The fourth option is *design*. This is the theistic option. The improbable state of the universe, constructed so as to allow life, is that way because it was designed that way. Purposeful intention underlies this extraordinary structuring. The designer did not design giraffes and elephants—she designed laws of physics that would lead to giraffes and elephants through the process of biological evolution.

I am claiming that you have a puzzle. The question is "Why is the universe constructed in this extraordinarily fine-tuned way which allows evolution to take place and us to come into existence?" The option which most of my astrophysical colleagues are promoting, is the second one. For instance the current writings of Martin Rees (the British Astronomer

Royal) deal with this concept of an ensemble of universes. The claim is that we exist because in that ensemble, if you have enough universes, it is highly probably that some of them will allow life to exist. We, therefore, live in one of those very special universes. That is their whole argument.

What I want to say here is that on considering these four principal metaphysical options, there is no way of scientifically proving one is right and the others are wrong. Metaphysical uncertainty remains. We cannot prove or disprove any of them. I have a colleague who believes in the pure chance idea, and there is no way to prove him wrong. However he can't prove he is right. The same is true for each of the other options. Option three is a bit of a dodgy one, because it just defers the essential issue. The main fundamental options are pure chance, very probable (normally based on an ensemble of universes which you can't test and can't prove exists), or the design option.

The point then is that *these are metaphysical options, and uncertainty is inherent in every option*. The uncertainty is inherent precisely because these are not physical options; they are metaphysical options. We have to make choices without sufficient evidence. We do not have any other possibility.

I have talked as much as I am going to for the moment about metaphysics. Now I want to turn to ethics at the top of the right hand side of Figure 1. Firstly, *there is a need for values*. Applied science always involves understanding and values. Values govern what we do. In environmental issues, in medicine, in biotechnology (particularly genetically modified crops, cloning, and gene therapy), in information technology, and in product design. There always are values that control what we do. This was my point in saying that ethics is the top of the causal hierarchy. The crucial point is that *science cannot provide morality*. Now some of my colleagues deny this, and I think they are wrong. The point that Monod[1] makes is that in order to do science, you have to have a certain level of honesty, you have to look at what's there and report it truthfully, and so on. Monod claims that these scientific virtues are the basis of all morality. Well, I just do not think he's thought about it sufficiently.

Everyday social life requires values that go far beyond these basic virtues. For instance, decisions about resource allocations or personal interactions cannot be governed by simple scientific virtues, which certainly are virtues. They are part of morality, but they are not the whole of morality. Science can tell us if some act will help further a particular goal. But it cannot tell us if that goal is good or not. Science can tell you if a particular policy will lead to the extinction of whales, but science cannot say whether the extinction of whales is good or is bad. Why not? Because there is no experiment that will give you an experimental value for "good." There are no units of "good" or "bad." There isn't a laboratory experiment that can tell you that this action was twenty "milli-Hitlers" bad, or something like that. There is no scientific experiment that can measure whether an outcome is good or evil; so there aren't any units for good or evil; and to talk about good and bad is simply beyond the domain of science. It is not part of what science can deal with.

So, science cannot provide values. It can help see what is there; what supports the basic scientific values. It cannot adjudicate on moral issues. It cannot adjudicate on whether "means" or "ends" are most important—whether intentions or results are what count. It cannot say how competing interests should be dealt with. It cannot deal with the issue of the right of the individual or the right of the group. I'm just indicating some specific issues which science, per se, cannot deal with. You have to make choices based on ethical standards you get from somewhere other than science. The conclusion is that science cannot provide any ethics. It cannot answer what is good or bad.

I want to go further than that and say that *science has failed us ethically*. There are major benefits to humanity from science, but a purely technological worldview goes badly astray in practice. We get pollution and environmental degradation. We get global warming. We get population growth, which is the driving force for all the environmental problems we have. These are unexpected consequences. So you can say, "Well science led to these but it is not what science intended to do, so it is not really an ethical problem." Or you can say that these are balanced by the good that science has done, and science has done an enormous amount of good in medicine, technology, and so on. So you can say they balance out, and science comes out OK. But, the failure of science is that it actually supports a purely technological world view, which does horrendous things in practice. This results in the development of nuclear weapons, which could lead to the end of the human race, the development of napalm (one of the most horrific things is the way that napalm was designed specifically to create the maximum terror and the maximum pain in the victim), and the development of biological weapons, which could lead to a horrible distortion of the human race. Remember the photograph of a Vietnamese Air Force plane dropping bombs of napalm on the Thrang Bang village…white phosphorus bombs exploding there and the famous picture of a young girl screaming in pain after the strike. This is where the scientific ethos will lead you if you do not do something about it. We may come to accept the solutions such as those of the Vietnam War, or of Kosovo, or of Hiroshima—which are fully in line with a Darwinian ethic. In this we lose our commitment to true ethics and seek an inhumane technological and scientific solution to a problem, which at its basis is not technological at all. Humane values depart from the scene.

One of the results of a technological worldview, which really interests me, is computer viruses. Somehow, the world of technology has accepted that there are people out there who write computer viruses. There is no mass movement in the world of information technology which says this is totally ethically unacceptable. It is an incredibly destructive behavior, which destroys many people's lives. The world of technology says, "Well, they are clever chaps. They're showing how technically good they are." And we pat them on the back a little bit and say "Tut, tut, you should not have done that." There is not that ethical outrage which there should be for the large scale destruction that computer viruses create. These are deliberate, purely destructive actions, which express and result from an underlying inhuman ethos.

So, I am emphasizing something with which you will all agree. I am emphasizing the central importance of meaningful action and ethical choices. The question is, "If science cannot provide it, where do we get our grounding?" There is one possible source that I will mention: the sociobiology option. There is a group of biologists who say that sociobiology explains our values and is an adequate explanation of ethics. But in my view, and in Nancey Murphy's view—and we write about it in our book— this does not explain morality ; this explains morality away. I'll return to that in just a minute. A second possible source for this grounding is to rely on culture and psychology, and this relativizes morality away. If you say that morality is based on psychology and cultural factors, then it is the society you grew up in which totally governs your ethical viewpoint. The issue then is exceedingly simple. What is acceptable in one culture is not the same as what is acceptable in another. If you take this viewpoint, you must say that what happened on September the eleventh of 2001, when the hijacked aircraft crashed into the World Trade Center, was just a clash of cultural viewpoints; there were no ethical issues involved. We must say that the group of people who conducted that action had one set of ethical standards and the people who did not do it had a different set, and that is all there is to say. If you say that ethics is based on cultural and psychological options, you are impotent to say that any action is evil.

The third alternative, which I then believe is the real one, is the *moral reality option*. This claims that there are, in fact, real values, and that we are able to say some acts are good and we are able to say some acts are evil. This is one of the intimations of a transcendent underlying domain.

First I want to say a little bit more about the sociobiology option. The idea here is that the ethical values we have result from a long epoch of evolution of prehumans and humans, hunter-gatherers, and that evolution built in certain values on which we can base our current ethics. Now that is a partial explanation, but it is not a total one, in my view. The first point is that every human activity has a sociobiology explanation. You can equally say the same applies to sociobiology and to physics— they both have sociobiology explanations, because if it applies in the one case, it applies in the other case. Well, I do not believe that sociobiology is a totally adequate explanation of physics, or even of sociobiology. This already makes it clear that sociobiology explanation is, at most, a partial explanation; it cannot be a full explanation. I will elaborate on this.

Physics, like every other human activity, has a grounding in sociobiology. But that does not undermine the validity of physics in its own right. It has a validity in its own terms. There are multiple explanations for the existence and form of physics. A part of this is a sociobiology explanation, as must be if this applies to every human activity (which is implicit in its nature). So the question is whether a single explanatory factor, such as sociobiology, suffices on its own to explain physics. Most of the explanation for the nature of physics is in terms of its own operations and validity. Physics has its own style of investigation and experimentation on which its validity as a scientific subject is based. That is, if we ask is it possible that, in the case of physics or of sociobiology itself, there is no other causal factor than sociobiology acting, the answer is clearly no In those cases it is obvious that this is not true, and I claim that the same is true for morality. Just as it is not a sufficient explanation for physics or sociobiology itself, sociobiology is not a sufficient explanation for morality either.

The second point is fundamental. If sociobiology were the total basis of morality then there would be no normative power. Let us consider that you are a person who believes sociobiology is the total origin and basis of morality. I ask you, "What does sociobiology tell me to do in response to the events of September the eleventh of 2001?" You will look at me a little blankly, and I am not sure what you might come up with. Perhaps you will say that the sociobiology ethical response is such and such. Then the fundamental question is, "Why should I obey that response?" That is, "Why is it a normative requirement on me to do it?", and there is no answer. Once you find a sociobiology explanation, you also understand that you have the choice whether or not to obey that, and it no longer has any normative power over you. Indeed sociobiology processes lead to both good and evil in an even-handed way. They have no power to say which is better or worse. It is true that sociobiology processes do indeed lead to moral behaviour of a certain kind—defending your children from threats for example. But that is just self-interest—which is not true morality. It has no status in terms of being right or wrong—it is just the fact that animals will defend their families even if it places themselves in peril. This is what I will call *low-level morality*, as opposed to the deep morality—the true morality—which I will now discuss.

Which morality am I referring to? What is the nature of true morality? That is a truly important question. I suggest there are four basic options. There is a *coercive morality* in which we will force you to behave the way we want you to by brutality, and many, many nations, rulers, and church people have, in effect, stated that this is the nature of morality. In fact, the early church, well from the year 1000 on, was largely ruled by coercive morality. There is a *reward* or *consumer morality*. If it is worth a lot, and if you can buy it, it is good. You can buy everything you want. And this is the current morality for a large part of America and the rest of the world. What counts is how much you own, how much you've got. There is the morality of *intellectual certainty*. If you cannot deny it, then it has to be moral. This position claims that you can argue intellectually about morality and make the choice in a purely rational fashion. That is a position which has failed and is bound to fail. Pure rationality cannor determine what is right and what is wrong —as explained above, morality is not a science. So, I together with Nancey Murphy and many others go for the fourth option, a *kenotic morality*—a morality of love and self-sacrifice, which is of a transforming nature. I will shortly say more about this.

These are the four options. You cannot prove that any one of them is correct by either science or philosophy, but, you can respond to the persuasive nature of any of them. And you can choose between them on metaphysical and religious grounds. To summarize, I have presented four options for the grounding of morality. These are:

1. Coercive morality
-we'll force you by brutality
2. Reward/consumer morality
-everything you want
3. Intellectual certainty
-you can't deny it
4. Kenotic morality
-love and self-sacrifice
(a transforming nature)

In these four options you will probably recognize the temptations of Christ in the desert. Options one, two, and three were the options that were considered and rejected by Christ. In fact, there is a beautiful description of this in the introduction of the book *Readings in St, John's Gospel* by William Temple. There he goes through the thought process of Christ in the desert considering options one, two, and three, rejecting each of them, and arriving at option four as the way he should lead his life.

So let me say more about *kenosis*. This is a joyous attitude that values love and justice; is generous and creative in pursuing these aims; and, if needed, is willing to give up personal necessities and to voluntarily sacrifice on behalf of others. This issue is that of *letting go on behalf of the greater good*. The point about kenosis is that this attitude of letting go has a transformational nature. There is the possibility of changing the quality and meaning of the situation facing us. Absolutely fundamental is the fact that this is probably the only way to true security and to peace because it is probably the only approach that has the capacity to change an enemy into a friend. I must emphasize this transformational quality. All the game theories, which some groups of psychologists are trying to tell us are the basis for morality, simply do not begin to comprehend the transformational nature of kenotic morality. This is because the whole point of kenotic reality is that whatever game you were playing before, kenosis completely changes the rules of that game. It transforms the whole nature of it.

Let me talk about kenosis briefly as a theme in life. The theme of mother and child is one of the most famous of these. A mother protects the child and is willing to give up her life on behalf of the child. But then, there are powerful instinctive drives for this. The much more difficult part is where the mother has to let the child go and let the child develop on its own and become an adult.

Kenosis is the foundation of community. If people in a community do not, to a considerable degree, submerge their own interests in favour of those of the community, the community won't function. Kenosis is the foundation of learning. When you want to understand something, physics or other subjects, you will come to that subject with preconceived ideas, which are your strongly-held ideas at the moment. You must let go of those preconceived ideas in order to be able to see what is actually there in front of you, and truly understand and react to it.

Kenosis is the foundation of true artistic endeavor. In developing a sculpture, a play, a novel, a painting, or whatever may be the object, the artist starts off with a preliminary idea, and begins putting it down and developing it. Then the piece begins to take shape. After a while it develops its own identity. At that stage the true artist is the person who responds to that identity with integrity and lets it go where it has to go because of its now autonomous nature. That is the difference between true art, deep art, as opposed to that produced by someone who tries to keep forcing a set of preconceived ideas even though they no longer fit what is now taking place in the work itself.

Kenosis is the basis of deep social action as exemplified by Mahatma Gandhi, Martin Luther King, Desmond Tutu, Ruby Bridges, and the Amy Biehl family.[2] It is giving up—letting go—of hate so you can see the opponent as a human being and respond with forgiveness. This theme of kenosis, of giving up, occurs in all the major religious faiths. I have done sufficient investigation to be convinced that this theme, which is certainly a central feature of Christianity (properly comprehended), is in the Jewish

Dresden after the fire-bombing, February 14, 1945. Photograph courtesy of Deutsche Fotothek, Dresden, Germany.

faith, the Muslim religion, the Hindu religion, and it is in the Japanese religions. It is my conviction that kenosis is central to all major religions. This is evident to those who truly open themselves up and see the core of the nature of that religious faith. I have here some quotations:

> An individual has not started living until he or she can rise above the narrow confines of his or her individualistic concerns to the broader concerns of all humanity. Every person must decide whether he or she will walk in the light of creative altruism or in the darkness of destructive selfishness. Life's

most persistent and urgent question is, " What are you doing
for others?"
—Martin Luther King Jr.

The deepest truth I have discovered is that if one accepts the
loss, if one gives up clinging to what is irretrievably gone, then
the nothing which is left [that which is left after kenosis] is not
barren but is enormously fruitful. Everything that one has lost
comes flooding back out of the darkness, and one's relation to it
is new - free and unclinging. But the richness of the nothing
contains far more, it is the all-possible, it is the spring of freedom.
—Robert Bellah (in *Beyond Belief*)

In looking at the transforming nature of kenotic action, the question
is what is most significant, the intentions or the consequences? Both
matter and are inter-related. Particularly, consequences seriously affect
the welfare of other people, the long-term viability of ecosystems, and so
on; there is a long-term effect of choices on ourselves, and ultimately, as
I am sure Nancey said, morality is about character development. Are we
developing a kenotic nature in ourselves so that it becomes second nature
to act in that way?—It becomes in-built when it becomes second nature.
It literally is in-built into the structure of your brain because the brain
connections get turned into a structure that has that nature. Or are you
letting your life be ruled by fear, resentment, and hate? If you are then
you will end up an empty and ruined hulk as the illustration here of
Dresden after the destruction of 1945 demonstrates. There were forty-
eight hours of fire bombing by the Allies, of a civilian city, which had no
military target of any consequence. This was probably the greatest and
most destructive fire of World War II. Seventy-five thousand civilian
people were burnt alive for no military purpose. So the people who had
set themselves up to fight the evils of the German aggression ended up
doing deeds which were just as bad.

So, we have metaphysics and ethics as the two "ultimate" issues,
and from what we have seen, one can make an interesting case to unify
them both. Of the four metaphysical options we have considered, one of
them—indeed one of the most satisfactory in logical terms - has a creator
or designer. This is a theological option. Of the ethical options, one of

them, again, is a theological option. So you can get a unified scheme in which theology is the basis for both the metaphysics and the ethics. This theological position is favored by an Ockham's Razor—it is the simplest way of uniting these in a single coherent scheme. Now of course, this is nothing other than one of the oldest theological views of human history. I have just been bringing back that very old theological view in a modern form. It maintains its coherence in this modern context.

I suggest that this view is supported by what I've called "intimations of transcendence." (Many other people have written about this: Peter Berger, C. S. Lewis, and so on.) These intimations of transcendence are:

- Morality, ethics
- Aesthetics, beauty
- Companionship, love
- Creativity, science
- Creation, existence
- Spiritual experience

Morality and ethics entails an understanding of the transforming nature of kenotic ethics. Aesthetics and beauty can be of a breathtaking nature, lifting us out of ourselves into a higher plane. I think those are hints of transcendent existence. Companionship and love can be taken to a point beyond themselves to something underlying—reflecting the nature of an underlying substratum of love. The nature of creativity which we see in science—the incredible creativity which leads to our amazing understanding—can be taken as a mirror of the creativity of the creator and hence an intimation of transcendence. The very fact of existence— the creation which has led to that existence and to our individual existence, the fact that we simply can be—can be taken as one of those signs. What are called spiritual experiences, this vast body of experience by many millions of people over the centuries, is an indication of something deeper underlying existence. You may recall that at the beginning of the first lecture I said that the events of everyday life are data about the universe just as much as scientific results are. These widespread spiritual experiences are one aspect of such data.

Now I want to try to indicate this nature of the intimations of transcendence by some examples:

I like to walk alone on country paths, rice plants and wild grasses on both sides, putting each foot down on the earth in mindfulness, knowing that I walk on the wondrous earth. In such moments, existence is a miraculous and mysterious reality. People usually consider walking on water or in thin air a miracle. But I think the real miracle is not to walk on water or in thin air, but on earth. Every day we are engaged in a miracle which we don't even recognise: a blue sky, white clouds, green leaves, the black, curious eyes of a child—our own two eyes. All is miracle.
- The Miracle of Mindfulness. T. N. Hanh.

I say to myself as I watch the niece, who is very beautiful: in her this bread is transmuted into melancholy grace. Into modesty, into a gentleness without words... Sensing my gaze, she raised her eyes towards mine, and seemed to smile. A mere breath on the delicate face of the waters, but an affecting vision. I sense the mysterious presence of the soul that is unique to this place. It fills me with peace, and my mind with the words: "This is the peace of silent realms." I have seen the shining light that is born of the wheat.
- *Flight to Arras.* Antoine de St. Exupery

[The talk was here illustrated by pictures of beautiful scenes of many kinds.] So I am suggesting that these can be taken as intimations of transcendence. The point is not just that they exist, but that when you see them in the true light there is an excess—there is more than is necessary. In the physical existence there didn't have to be such beauty and such grace. There is a unifying kenotic theme in all of this. So, to put this into our ontological scheme, we add to the worlds I've previously talked about a *Meta-world five*—a world of ultimate reality—which is the source of meaning, purpose, and ethics. That completes the sets of worlds. This is, of course, the world of God. It is effective by creation and revelation.

So the key idea of such a synthesis, which I have said is a very old idea, is that *the fundamental aim of loving action is to shape the nature of creation and transcendence in practice, setting their meaning, implications, and limitations.* The meaning of the phrase "in practice" is that the Creator could have ordered things differently, but has voluntarily and freely specifically restricted the nature of creation to that required for this purpose of allowing loving action to take place through moral agency. In this synthesis we take seriously the concept that the purpose of the universe is precisely to make this kind of sacrificial response possible, and pursue the implications. This hypothesis may be tested by its consequences.

Assume that your hypothesis is that such a synthesis exists. You ask then where it will lead you. If you are the creator and you want to create a universe where loving self-existing beings can respond with love, how would you do it?

First, there is a need for the creation of a Universe in which ordered patterns of behaviour exist, for without this, free will (if it can be attained) cannot function. If there were no rules or reliable patterns of behaviour governing the activity of natural phenomena, it would not be possible to have a meaningful moral response to the happenings around one. Thus the material world, through which sentient beings are realised, needs to be governed by repeatable and understandable patterns. Morality cannot exist without a reliable framework in which to take place.

Second, we would require that these laws and regularities allow the existence of intelligent beings, who can sense and react in a conscious way, and who furthermore have effective free will. The word "effective" here means that whatever the underlying mechanisms governing human life are, there must be a meaningful freedom of choice which can be exercised in a responsible way. For without this, the concept of ethics is meaningless. Necessarily, all the restrictions implied by the Anthropic Principle as conditions for the existence of life must then be fulfilled.

The *third* requirement is that rain falls alike on believer and unbeliever, and makes the existence of both possible. This is achieved by the impartial operation of the laws of physics, chemistry, and biology, offering to each person alike the bounty of nature irrespective of their beliefs or moral condition. This mode of operation of the physical world thus fulfils the condition of freeing men and women from a need for obedience to God in order to survive, and so makes a free and unconstrained response possible.

The *fourth* requirement is that the created world can not be dominated by God himself, striding the world and demanding obedience on pain of punishment, or dominated by explicit marks of his activity so that belief in his existence and nature would be forced on everyone. For then they could not deny God's existence and the resulting demand on their ways of behaviour. In those cases, faith is not an option. You are forced to believe in God. Freedom from such a situation is again satisfied through the nature of creation as we see it, governed by impartial physical laws, which nevertheless allow a free and open response to those hints as to God's true nature that are given us.

Finally, despite the hidden nature of the underlying reality, it must still be open to those who wish to discern this true nature and to receive encouragement to follow the true way. Indeed, on the view taken here, it is the wish of God that they should do so. Firstly, it should be possible to make specific intimations of this reality available to those who are ready to receive them. And secondly, there should be available to all, as a basis for ethics, a mode of revelation of a more broadly based appreciation of what is right and wrong, of what is good and bad.

So those are five things that one might ask for in order to create a universe where there is an existence of free moral agents who can respond with love. *Kenosis* is the freedom to serve through self-emptying, but what is its purpose? As time goes on, the self becomes emptied, but the purpose must be *theosis*—the power to be and serve through participation in the divine being (literally this should be the divine "be-ing.") grows. That is, as time goes on, divine participation grows. The development of a faith—involves the joint development of kenosis and theosis. With time, the self is emptied, and participation with the divine being grows.

What is the nature of the evidence for all of this? We're not dealing with a repeatable situation as in a scientific investigation. To some extent we're dealing with almost repeatable situations, as in psychology, and the intimations of transcendence. But the true keys to revelation are unique situations—once only situations—as in the case of the historical sciences. The appropriate investigation is then historical rather than experimental. We have here the scandal of the particularity of religion. Important personal and religious experience may be given to us only once via unique revelatory events. That of course is one of the major tensions with science. Science does not want to look at unique revelatory events but at repeatable ones.

A full investigation of the religious option must take this situation seriously. Revelatory events are individual events and not repeatable.

That is true in personal life as well as in the life of the world. The issue of testing the evidence is crucial here. The crucial feature to any belief system is testing the evidence—rigorously checking for self-delusion. In both the scientific and religious cases we check in terms of text, traditional authority, and community balanced against each other. We test them in terms of their fruits—what consequences do they lead to? We test them in terms of impartiality, which is the kenotic theme again. We think we know what the answer is, but we give up the need to believe we know the answer. We let go and see if the conclusion still remains. Finally, we test overall consistency and coherency.

What I think we can claim is that the overall kind of world picture that I have presented is coherent and consistent. But, the choice is individual, and inescapable. There is no proof, I've already emphasized that. There is no logical proof that any of the options is correct. But there is a coherence one might find compelling. What are the alternatives that I am rejecting? I'm rejecting soft science—views which do not take science seriously. I'm rejecting coercive religion. I am rejecting dogmatic atheism. And I'm rejecting all fundamentalisms. What I claim are open alternatives are:

a) *Non-dogmatic atheism.* An atheism which says, "I am an atheist, but I admit that other options are open."
b) *Agnosticism,* which refuses to take a stand. This is a perfectly viable position although it is rather unsatisfying.
c) *Non-dogmatic theism.* This is a theism that says, "I believe strongly, based on my own personal experience and conviction, that this is the truth. But I do understand that I cannot prove that it is the truth."

What are the implications, realizing that certainty is unattainable? Because there is no certainty, in order to live a worthwhile life, a covenant with faith is needed whereby one chooses one or other of these options, because one cannot live without faith. For those adopting the theistic option, this choice will be mainly because of their own personal experience but they can be assured that there is indeed a viable intellectual position available to support this view, as outlined in these talks.

The first challenge is testing something like the vision I've been putting forth and developing a corresponding understanding of the nature of ultimate reality. That is where interfaith dialogue is fascinating and important because that is where you incorporate the other views humanity has developed as well as our own tradition. The second challenge lies in being aware of this whole set of interlocking themes that are discussed here, of seeing the whole. I claim that as true spirituality. True spirituality recognizes the interlocked reality, which God has given us—the spiritual and the material, the practical and the intellectual, the physical and chemical nature of our existence as well as community and ethics, love and forgiveness, and some kind of relation within God. This interlocking set of issues makes a whole incorporating what we consider to be the ethereal, which is often the revelation, and the concrete. True spirituality is not just those several experiences which some people call spiritual, but it is seeing this entire interlocking whole, because this interlocking whole is what God has created and wishes.

Where does this lead? It should lead to transforming the future. It means understanding the present—seeing things as they are. It means a transforming vision—seeing what truly might be. And then transforming action—which will, in my view, be based on the power of love and kenosis. And then making it happen through determination and courage. Spirituality in action will involve caring for the poor and the weak. It will involve using scientific and technological vision to help transform their lives by providing water, food, energy, work, and income of some kind. It will provide the poor and the weak with access to the information and communications the rest of us have already, and particularly to education and understanding. True spirituality will require asking, as one engages in such action, "Who is it that benefits?" Particularly in an international context we must ask who will benefit from these actions.

Here is the core:

If you are confused about what has gone wrong and how to fix it. Well listen. This is what Yahweh asks of you, only this: to act justly, to love tenderly, and to walk humbly with your God.
- Micah 6:8

Here are some of the dangers. Firstly there is *fundamentalism*—a desperate hanging on to some partial truth, treated as if it were the whole truth. At least one must acknowledge there may be some partial validity in other approaches than one's own. In particular, one should not mistake one's models of reality for reality itself. No model, image, or theory can comprehend the whole of reality. Second there is a tendency towards a *lack of involvement*—developing an academic understanding that avoids human engagement. A main reason we have been given understanding is in order that we can become effectively engaged.

So the future vision which I have is, on the one hand, a wider awareness by scientists of the breadth and dimensions of cause, existence, and evidence as I have outlined it, and on the other side, a wider scientific awareness by the public at large of the scientific side of things—that incredible body of understanding which is also an extraordinary achievement of humanity—with a developing ability to see the larger whole that takes this into account. And, a common commitment to develop such larger visions and apply them towards a better society.

So we need science in the service of humanity as one of the key objectives. The future key issues will include:

- Information technology
- Biotechnology
- Environment and sustainability
- Global warming and weather
- Value-based human sciences and medicine
- The brain and consciousness, which is one of the most important areas of study and understanding at the moment which will have tremendous ethical implications we are going to have to tackle.

We will require testing and the establishment of institutional safeguards which will make all of this happen in an ethically desirable way. We are going to have to face:

- Anti-science extremism of various kinds
- Fundamentalist environmentalism
- Religious fundamentalism
- Adherents of soft science, not taking the scientific method seriously

We are going to have to get a commitment to:

- Global sustainability
and some commitment to do something about
- Global war and peace

- A just global dispensation
- Caring for the poor and weak
- Caring for each other

I am trying to indicate here that this kenotic vision is not something that has no implications. It has tremendous implications for what we should be out there doing. I am just flagging them as issues, which are implied by this kind of kenotic vision. In other words we must be working for *a just, peaceful, and sustainable society* (JPSS).

So a reprise on the worlds of existence is as follows: World 1 is the world of matter and forces. World 2 is the world of consciousness. World 3 is the world of Aristotelian possibilities—the world of possibilities from which the real world is chosen. World 4 is the world of Platonic reality—which somehow underlies the world and helps control it. World 5 is the Meta-world of meaning and ethics—the world of God, which is the fundamental underlying reality, incorporating purpose based on love. These are all simultaneously present and simultaneously active if you take this overall coherent view. A purely material view of the nature of existence is immensely poverty stricken when compared with what one can claim actually is.

Isaac Pennington (1653) expresses some of this in a beautiful way:

All Truth is shadow except the last, except the utmost; yet every Truth is true in its own kind. It is substance in its own place, though it be but shadow in another place (for it is but a reflection from an intenser substance); and the shadow is a true shadow, as the substance is a true substance.

And a reprise on the kenotic life is found in the Bhagavad Gita, as quoted by Mahatma Ghandi:

He is forever free who has broken out of the ego-cage of I and mine to be united with the Lord of Love. This is the supreme state. Attain thou this and pass from death to immortality.

And George Fox (founder of the Quakers) said, "Walk cheerfully over the world, responding to the Light of God in every person."

The Science and Religion Debate

George F. R. Ellis
9:00 am, Sunday, April 14, 2002

I want to talk about three things today:

- Current issues
- Important areas for development

and briefly about

- Integral studies and true spirituality

A: The Past

This is probably very familiar to you, but I just wanted to set the scene. There's been conflict between science and religion in the past and in a sense the main reason is that in turn each has dominated and claimed more than it should have, and then has had to, or will have to, pull back.

Religion has in the past claimed too much in many ways, but particularly in relation to scientific knowledge and a relation to certainty. It has now had to retract or it is in the process of retracting. Scientific progress in understanding causal mechanisms has been truly amazing, encompassing most areas of life, and we have talked a lot about that. As a consequence some scientists have started claiming too much for science and I have in mind the names of Atkins,[1] Dennett,[2] Dawkins[3] and Sagan,[4] as well as Monod.[5] In particular "some have claimed that their turf includes ethics and metaphysics providing a third culture rendering visible the deeper meaning of our lives and redefining who and what we are." That's from a book called *The Third Culture: Beyond the Scientific Revolution* by John Brockman. Well, this is all an illusion because science cannot do it, and I have talked in the previous sessions about the limits to science.

B: The Present

At the present there is a growing recognition of mutuality with an increasing science and religion dialogue taking place. Incidentally, I think the Templeton Foundation has played a huge role in this. The struggle has been to try to persuade the academic world that the science and religion debate is a respectable academic subject. I think that a huge amount of progress has been made in that way in recent times. This debate recognizes that the major areas of concern of science and religion are indeed separate and in the main no conflict arises between them. Science dealing with how, and religion with why. Science with what is, and religion with what ought to be.

Options

Now at the present time some claim there is indeed there is still a real conflict, with science dominant. This is the position of Atkins, Dennett, Dawkins and various other people. I probably should add that there almost certainly is also a converse claim with some religious people claiming religion is dominant, but they are not making a huge headway in the world out there where science is taken very seriously.

Now others claim there is a possibility of peaceful coexistence, with the famous idea of non-overlapping magisteria proposed by Stephen Jay Gould. Science is over here and religion is over there and there is not any interface and therefore there is not any conflict because they do not deal with the same domain. Now, although they do not deal with the same domain, I think this is an illusion because there are areas where there is indeed conflict or potential conflict.

Finally, others claim some kind of integration is possible to give a unified world view that accommodates both without diluting either. This is the kind of picture which I have been trying to put forward, but I must note this is not the same as E.O. Wilson's "consilience," which is in effect science taking over religion and not only religion, but a great many other things as well. So the kind of thing that I am talking about is a consilience, but it is not the consilience described in the book by E.O. Wilson. Wilson's consilience is simply a claim that science is dominant, although it is disguised.

Previous Conflict

Now there are areas that used to be sites of conflict, but in my view no longer are for those who are at the forefront of research or who fully understand the situation. There is a group who has not arrived at this understanding. But for those who are seriously in the debate, areas of previous conflict are no longer important. These include *firstly* the origins of the universe. The mechanism of the evolution of the universe, the origin of large-scale structures in it, indeed the whole of cosmology and the existence of a physical big bang or steady-state universe, comprised a domain of conflict. In fact this was what led Fred Hoyle to develop the steady-state universe. In old statements from the Pope there was the same kind of reliance on the idea that a big bang was consistent with God and the steady state wasn't. I think we now understand that this was all a big mistake and that whether there was a big bang or not is independent of the existence of God. Of course one can say that Augustine understood this already a thousand years ago.

Secondly, the origins of life. This is much more controversial. In these talks I have advocated Darwinian evolution as the underlying mechanism for the origin of life. In this evolutionary processes replace special design. We no longer think that God designed giraffes and zebras and butterflies. We rather think now that God designed the laws of physics which then led through a series of causal processes to giraffes, zebras and butterflies. There is a rear guard-action taking place here that denies this, and there is indeed a possible time-scale problem we could perhaps talk about. But I do not think that this is where the serious debate is taking place, and the main vanguard of the science and religion debate is elsewhere. There is of course the "intelligent design" debate. However, part of the reason I haven't gotten involved in that myself, and haven't seriously tried to understand Dembski[6] et al, is that I think this is the wrong ground to fight over; I simply don't think that it helps in the science and religion debate to concentrate on this.

Unresolved Underlying Issues

There are deeper underlying issues that remain unresolved or about which there is current active debate. Here there is indeed potential conflict and a striving for resolution.

1. Existence. The first is the issue of existence: the metaphysics and ontology of cosmology that I have talked about. It is not the mechanisms of cosmology that are important. We do not care whether there is a steady-state in the universe or not. Either way, there is still an underlying debate about cosmological existence. The issue of design and creation return at a higher level in the relation to the laws of physics themselves and in particular to the anthropic issue, which I raised earlier. Why is the universe such as to allow any process of evolution whatever? We can see this argument leading to the metaphysical options I laid out earlier. Martin Rees and his colleagues are saying that they understand that there is a problem; they understand that there is tremendous fine-tuning of the universe as we see it. So they advocate the idea of an ensemble of universes, which I mentioned before. However that is not actually a scientific theory; that is a metaphysical theory—it is unprovable. There are also people including myself and my colleague Nancey Murphy, who say that there could be a principle of design here, underlying the nature of the laws of physics and, hence, leading to the existence of humanity. There is, therefore, a debate about the issue of existence, particularly the issue of an existence which allows us almost inevitably to evolve from the laws of physics once we are given those laws of physics.

2. Being Human. The second, and in many ways the most difficult issue, is that of being human. What is our essential nature in the light of modern biology and in particular in the light of molecular biology and present-day neuroscience? Now here is a very, very active debate. This concerns particularly the related issues of free will and the nature of the soul, and the question of resurrection and the afterlife. The underlying issue is the nature and implications of reductionism, about which I have, in effect, said a great deal. This whole debate has immensely important application, for instance, in medical ethics and medicine, because how you view people is crucial to how you treat them. Particularly important in this is the issue of free will. If we believe that people have no free will, because we consider things from a strictly scientific causation point of

view, then the whole of morality is undermined. My research supervisor Dennis Sciama for instance, took this position. I used to tease Dennis about this. He would say, look there isn't free will, it is an illusion. Then we would go into a meeting of the astrophysics sector at Trieste and we would start talking about people we wanted to bring into the sector. And he would say, "Well, he is a responsible person." I would then turn to him and say, "If you say he is a responsible person, that contradicts entirely what you just said about there being no such thing as free will," and he would sort of harrumph about it and not actually solve it.

In my view any scientific theory which leads you to say free will is an illusion, is clearly in contradiction of a mass of evidence and, therefore, should be rejected. There are many cognitive scientists who will not agree with me, but Anton Zeilinger, at the Wheeler (Celebration for John Archibald Wheeler) meeting about three weeks ago in Princeton said that science doesn't make sense if there is no free will. This is because the scientist presumes he has the free will to choose what experiment to do and then to analyze that experiment without having the outcome of that analysis determined in some mechanical sense. Anton Zeilinger was very strong on that saying that if free will is not true, physics doesn't make sense as an enterprise. But much more controversial perhaps is this whole issue of the nature of the soul, which Nancey Murphy has talked about. Does the whole nature of current neuroscience say there is no such thing as the soul? I have no proper view on this except to say that I believe that the freeing up of ontology I was presenting helps to make room for the idea of a soul. If you stick only with my World 1, which is what a fundamentalist materialist will do, and you don't take into account the other worlds, then you are much more able to say there is no such thing as a soul. If you say the other worlds, that is the Worlds 2, 3, and 4, which I have presented, must be taken seriously even by science, then you have loosened things up to a degree so that the idea of a soul is no longer such a far-off idea from the concerns of science.

Resurrection and the afterlife is an issue of importance. Again I do not have a specific stand on this that I am going to present to you. I am simply flagging this as a serious issue. Does modern understanding of the nature of humanity say resurrection is impossible and afterlife is impossible? Of course a position one can take is simply to say that God can choose, at some point or other, to call an end to the old laws of physics and bring in new laws. In some sense that is a total answer, which may

or may not satisfy you. One may perhaps say one does not want to
have a resurrection of that kind. One wants a resurrection and an
afterlife, which are compatible with the current laws of physics. Then
you are in much greater trouble, or you may perhaps say that the idea
of transcendence should be taken seriously. You may say that God
lives in a totally different dimension and has a totally different kind of
existence. Then whatever concept you have of the resurrection and
the afterlife takes place in that totally different kind of creational
existence and not in the present one, which is more or less the position
of C. S. Lewis in his lovely book *The Great Divorce*. Well, these are
debatable and I am not trying to solve them. I am just saying there are
a lot of options, which are available.

3. Religious Experience. The next topical issue I would bring before
you is that of religious experience, which I have mentioned once or twice
in these talks, and the interpretation of ethical and spiritual data. Is it all
delusion? Is it all self-constructed? Or does it in some way relate to reality?
Is revelation, spiritual revelation, real or imaginary? Now I think it is
quite clear and we must face the fact that a great deal of what is claimed
as spiritual relation is delusion. And you can get a very strong sense of
that by going into any average bookshop and finding a section that is
labeled "spirituality." If you look at the kind of stuff that is in there, you
will find that a lot of it is, well, weird. So the question is how do we
separate out delusional aspects from the real? Let's assume that some is
real. How do we go about separating them out? This is a major issue, but
of course it is an age-old problem for the church and those in the church.
Was Joan of Arc deluded or not? Was Saul of Tarsus deluded on the road
to Damascus? And so on. The position, which I have taken in this, is to
claim that if we take religion seriously, then there is some spiritual data,
which is genuine and is not delusional. In my view, if you don't believe
that then you could put forward a view of religion, as I think the spiritual
naturalists like Ursula Goodenough do, in which there is no channel of
communication of any kind from some entity one might call God into
the human brain. If there is no such channel then all so-called religious
experience is self-constructed. There would then be no external referent,
necessarily, for religious experience and, therefore, in my view, religion
itself would then be a delusion.

So I think this is a very important topic. There are two kinds of issues or questions here. First, how does a religious community discern the true from the false? That is an age-old debate which we could take up, perhaps. There is a huge amount of experience in the religious world, but there is also a huge amount of evidence of error. Particularly, for example, when the Catholic Church claims that the Pope is infallible, then you have a delusion set down in writing. The second question is: how within the context of the laws of physics could there be such a channel? We have already considered this in some of our discussions. I am one of the people who take the position that quantum uncertainty provides a perfectly open way for a strong spiritual person to say that physics could provide such a channel, and I believe that no physicist could prove that you are wrong. There are other routes which have been suggested. For example John Polkinghorn advocates chaos as the route, and Arthur Peacocke advocates top-down action. Nancey Murphy and I have both written in various places that we do not believe that these routes will provide the precise kind of channel that is needed. There is a further, but totally separate issue. Suppose that there is such a channel available to God. In what way would he or she use it? This is a very serious kind of concern and it is a theological concern. What kind of intimations of transcendence would give people that understanding which enables them to respond to God's kenotic nature without forcing them to do so? I think that it can be understood reasonably well, and the kind of picture I have been trying to present fits in with that.

4. God's Action. The further and deeply related issue is that of God's action in the world. This has been the theme of the Vatican/CTNS Series of meetings which has been going on for ten years and has led to a set of five books which are available from the Vatican Observatory and CTNS.

Does God act in the world apart from creating it and maintaining the laws of physics and action? If so, in what manner, and how can this be compatible with the scientific understanding of causation? I am flagging this as an important issue. There is an entire spectrum of positions on this issue. Some people say, "Yes, miracles can take place and there is no problem because God controls the laws of physics. God can suspend them if He or She wants to." At the other end people contend that God created the world and created the laws of physics and thereafter does not interfere in any way. God is the passive observer. Then there is the middle position, which I have been suggesting, in which God does interact, but only through persuasive mental images. Why? Because it is our hands that are God's hands in this world and only our hands are God's hands. So there is this whole range of options and you will have your own views on this and I may be treading on someone's theological toes in the way I am presenting this. In which case I apologize.

5. Reductionism and Modern Science. The major underlying issue in a lot of this is reductionism in light of modern science and this is what I have concentrated on in these talks I have given. What is the true nature of reductionism and its implications? Central here is the nature of causation and explanation in complex hierarchically structured systems, where there are multiple levels of causality and action. I have talked in depth about this. There is the relation between bottom-up and top-down action in such systems. There is also the relation between the evolutionary process on the one hand and cultural, social, and psychological processes on the other, in terms of the structure of the brain and the way that we act. I have said a lot about this already in the first couple of lectures, so I will not say much here except to indicate that I do think this is a crucial issue, and that is why I have been putting quite a lot of effort into it. Related to this is the nature of existence and ontology, which again I have said quite a lot about in these lectures. So I am not going to say more about that here except to state that this is clearly a very important theme and I am hoping that the kind of viewpoint which I was presenting embraces this. As I have emphasized, this viewpoint is developed from the ideas of Roger Penrose. There is a lovely little book by Roger Penrose called *The Small, the Large and the Human Mind*. It is a book one should look at if one wants to understand his views on this. There are also the books by Popper[7] and Eccles[8] which are their views on this nature of ontology. In a sense what I have given is just a synthesis of the ideas of Penrose on the one hand, and the ideas of Popper and Eccles on the other. Incidentally what I have not done is try to relate this to the world of Teilhard de Chardin. Teilhard may have very well been saying much of what I have been saying but in a different language. I would bow to other people's knowledge in that respect.

6. Nature of Existence. Given the nature of ontology, what is crucial is the relation of epistemology to ontology, that is the relation of knowledge to existence, particularly in the case of religious knowledge. Now I do not find interesting the debate on post-modernism and

relativism, basically because I think that debate is intrinsically incoherent. If you take a strong post-modernist position you have no leg to stand on if you apply your own analysis to yourself. So I just do not have a position in this debate. There may be some philosophers who will say I am being too quick about it.

I have emphasized in the manner in which I have spoken, and I will re-emphasize, that I think one of the major mistakes which philosophers keep making is to confuse ontology with epistemology. Certainly that was the mistake of the 1930s made by A. J. Aire and other people. It is absolutely clear from astrophysics that just because you cannot see something does not mean that it is not there. The example, which is absolutely clear, is that in the standard models of cosmology matter exists beyond the visual horizon. We do not have any information about that matter. We never will have any information, but that does not mean that it does not exist. That example alone should suffice to demonstrate that something can be present even though we cannot see it.

There are difficult issues about epistemology and ontology in quantum mechanics, the foundation of physics, and I have no serious answer to that. The fundamental and simple issue is that one must not confuse epistemology and ontology. As I have pointed out, I think that is one of the major mistakes through the course of the history of philosophy. There is also an important sub-debate. Does ontology matter? There is the religious naturalism movement that takes a very curious stand on this. Ursula Goodenough outlines her position in her book *The Sacred Depths of Nature*, which roughly speaking is that she is a biologist and has a position as a naturalist. She treats religious life as if it has meaning, although she does not seem to believe that there is a God who underlies religious life. To me this is an incoherent position, but there is a whole movement out there that believes this. I have probably not understood it properly.

The Eternal Issues Remain

I identify here:

- Freewill
- Evil
- The nature of God's action in the world
- Discernment distinguishing truth from deception

I put in evil there because it always will come up. Of course evil is not specifically related to science. However, parts of the issue of evil in the world may be related to science in the sense, which Polkinghorne has suggested, and to which I hinted: If you create the laws of physics so that people can come into existence who do have free will, then it may very well be that what we call evil will be a necessary consequence.

C: The future

The debate can be expected to grow with the establishment of academic standards in this area supported by public debate, lectures, meetings, journals, books, and societies. This is what is presently taking place, but I think it is very important to understand that the serious debate is going to be very international and interfaith. Indeed, this debate is an excellent meeting ground between the faiths, including atheism as a faith. Here there is a sound basis for interfaith discussions, enabling consideration of important issues, which are faith issues, but without a head-on clash of faith fundamentals, and I think it is already serving this purpose. For example, the "Science and the Spiritual Quest" series of meetings is engaging faiths across the spectrum in this dialogue in a very interesting way. There is an underlying kind of tension here, which is not often discussed. Once one enters the interfaith movement there is a necessary need to give up any claim that our religion is the only one and you are damned if you are not following after it. Many people have moved beyond that point to a position where they claim that all faiths provide some kind of light on the nature of God—they are simply different, valid ways of going about relating to God. Each religion has a particular historical context and so on, and they are all equally valid.

I think that is the way much of the interfaith movement is going, but in the end that is not good enough because there are some faiths that are not acceptable, and that is a difficult point. A serious question for this interfaith movement in general, and for the interfaith movement related to science and religion in particular, is whether you have standards for which faiths you will accept and which you will not. Are there people you would exclude from this dialogue, and if there are, on which criteria will exclusion be based? Firstly there is the truth requirement. Anybody who is going to take part in this dialogue, from any faith, will have to be willing to look at the evidence. The basic demand of science is that we look at the evidence and see what it tells us. In other words we cannot enter into interfaith debate with anybody who says my divine book has the truth and that is it, and I am not looking at any other evidence. Any such person is not able to take part in this debate. But there are also ethical questions. The history of religion is full of evil caused by religion. There are still religious sects who are causing manifest evil in the world. Would you include them also in your search for an interfaith dialogue? I would say no, so I am opposed to a universalist position which accepts all. If you are entering the interfaith dialogue you have to kenotically give up the dominant position of your religion as being the ultimate truth. You simply cannot start an interfaith dialogue unless you accept that in some sense the religious viewpoint of the other is a serious engagement with God as the fundamental reality. However, you have to insist that those you engage with take evidence seriously and are not actively engaged in promoting evil.

The Main Divide

There are deep metaphysical or philosophical divisions between the theists, and nontheists, and among the theists, and so on. But a main divide, which I see, is not any of those. The main division is between the fundamentalists and the non-fundamentalists of each faith. In my view in each of the faiths there is a fundamentalist group and a non-fundamentalist group. We can engage with the non-fundamentalist, but we cannot engage seriously with the fundamentalists of any religion, because they are not open to discussion.

The former, the fundamentalists, have closed minds based on a desperate clinging to partial truths, which are proclaimed as total truths. The latter, the non-fundamentalists, by and large, are open-minded to complexity and acknowledge doubt and uncertainty, the limits of language and perception, and the insights of others. We can enter into debate with the latter group but not the former. The former cannot meaningfully take part in the science and religion dialogue. The latter can and indeed must do so in order to remain fully relevant to the changing cultural scene.

The Basic Triad

The further point, which is made by Nancey [Murphy] and myself is that the basic triad is not just science and religion, it is science, ethics and religion. I find puzzling the attempts by some people to have a science and religion dialogue that doesn't include ethics in the triad, because I think the dialogue is going to be very incomplete without ethics. In fact the debate is incomplete and inconclusive without including all three. Thus the debate must take cognizance of science, which studies the mechanisms of how things interact; religion, which studies why and the issues of meaning and spirituality; and ethics which asks what to do. Only in considering all of these does the debate become real.

A really interesting question, which came up in this debate briefly yesterday, is the question of whether this base should include aesthetics. Should there be a fourth part of this base saying aesthetics is very important? That is a really interesting question. I have avoided this so far because in the case of ethics I claim that I can see the strand of kenosis, which runs through all religions. I cannot see an aesthetic strand, which is not totally culturally dependent, and I stand to be corrected in that.

Integral Vision 1

Some time ago, after considering all of this, I put together a proposal for an Institute of Integral Studies that could try to develop all of this by looking at various things. This institute would consider a number of different areas.

A. Foundational Issues: Image, Reality, and Integral Visions.

The first area includes the foundational issues having to do with image, reality and integral visions. It would look at ontology and epistemology and the relations of image to reality, which I have talked about in considerable depth. This is where the interfaith dialogue is important. When a principal part of the issue is expressed in terms of the relation of image to reality, it becomes important to inquire into what kinds of images human beings can have of a transcendent reality. Well, it is safe to say that they can have a huge variety of images of that reality and this is easily one way of looking at the whole interfaith issue. There are the issues of reductionism, emergent order and its implications, which we talked a lot about. And then there is the issue of integral visions: analytic and experiential. What I am hoping will emerge out of this debate is the ability on a growing scale for people to intellectually understand this vast interlocking reality that is presented to us not only intellectually but also experientially. That is really, really an interesting kind of question. How do you experientially start to look at some of this, instead of just in a purely academic way?

I will just briefly mention one thing, which I find absolutely fabulous. Brian Swimme's book on the cosmos, which some of my colleagues do not like, has what I regard as an absolutely terrific way of trying to help people start relating to the cosmos. He does this in the following way. On a starlit night he asks you to lie down on the grass and look up at the dark sky. Remember that you are on this ball with only gravity holding you there. If the gravity let go you would fly off into space. Or think of yourself on the earth with the universe you see not above you but below you. Then if the gravity let go you would fall down into the night sky, which you see there below you. It is a rather lovely kind of experiment through which you get a feel for how gravity is holding you onto the earth and if it let go you wouldn't be held onto the surface of the earth. I think it is really interesting, with this kind of integrated view, to try to think experientially of where art comes in. That includes visual art, music, ballet, and so on.

B. Developmental Issues: Society and Ethics.

The second area for consideration by this integral studies institute involves developmental issues. It would consider how this fundamental world-view plays out in society and ethics, because if this is a serious basis for understanding, it is a serious basis for life and it must have practical implications. That link is crucial. One of the things that can be done here is an inquiry into progress in global ethics and practice in the last millennium. In my opinion there is not sufficient understanding of the incredible progress which has been made in practical ethics in the real world in the last thousand years. There is not sufficient understanding of how human rights, women's rights, and animal's rights have all progressed an unbelievable amount. If you look back at the long-term history of humanity it is clear that in the last thousand years, and specifically in the last hundred years, democracy has made unbelievable strides.

Another issue is that of ethics and values in public policy and technological practice. There are obvious implications here for bioethics and medicine. Particularly as we increase our understanding of the brain we acquire the power to interfere with the brain because we understand its function more and more. Enormous ethical issues will subsequently emerge. And something in which I have been very interested and have done some writing and thinking about is the issue of indices of quality of life or well-being for society and their use in public debate. In the modern world, because of its complexity, vast decisions are made on the basis of certain indices like productivity, balance of payments, unemployment, gross domestic product, and so on. These are the measures that motivate policy makers, but they only reflect restricted economic issues. The really interesting question is what is a good set of indicators of quality of life and welfare that should be used in public policy.

C. Religious and Ethical Issues: Discernment, Kenosis, and Hope.

The third area deals with religious and ethical issues: discernment, kenosis and hope. I have already mentioned the central question of the methods of discernment and testing in religion and ethics. I think it is so important that much more should be written about it than I have seen. There is the issue of kenosis and forgiveness in world religions and practice. I have been talking about kenosis. But how does it work out in practice? Is it practical in private individual lives and communal lives? On what scales is kenosis actually practical? We had an interesting discussion that started on that road last night. As I have said, this study would take a great serious look at Mahatma Gandhi, Martin Luther King, Nelson Mandela, and Desmond Tutu. It would look at the Forgiveness and Reconciliation Commission and so on, and so on. Is kenosis practical? If so, how is it practical? Relating to this are ways of handling divisions of opinion in religion and ethics. In the real world one will get certain amounts of agreement, but when we get disagreement, how will one handle that?

There are, finally, issues of hope and reality. This is actually a quite important issue. In my country in the past thirty years, there were many times when there seemed to be absolutely no hope. People kept on despite the logical conviction that we were never going to get anywhere - and in the end hope triumphed over rationality. And this is a much broader issue. It could come into play in terms of the future of humanity which some of us were talking about. Is humanity doomed? How long is humanity going to survive on this earth, given the power of technological destruction?

D. Making a Difference

Finally, putting together an integral vision studies project of this kind, I would want there to be an action section, which will actually try to test and put into practice some of these ideas. This section would be related in some way to practical issues. First there would be the creation of an ever-widening informed community of concern, engaged in networking and community building. Secondly, some action projects, in which one tried out these ideas in practice, would be undertaken in developed countries and underdeveloped countries. In this way we would see if these were just pie-in-the-sky ideas or if they could actually work in some serious way.

True Spirituality

I just want to comment again on my view of true spirituality. I have already commented that if you go into an average bookshop and look in the section on spirituality you will find a lot of extraordinarily dubious stuff to do with astrology, pyramids, flying saucers, the Bermuda Triangle, and so on. In my view real spirituality lies in the openness and awareness that takes all relative human experiences and understanding seriously and sees in them, at least dimly, glimpses of the transcendent nature of an underlying reality. It encompasses all these aspects and much more. In other words, a true spirituality would have science as part of it. After all, if you believe in God as the creator, then God created physics and chemistry and astrophysics and God is thus a scientist. So that is part of the nature of God. But there is always the ethical side, the artistic side and so on. So my view of true spirituality does not lie just in that part of what people see as spirituality—prayer and contemplation—although it certainly includes them. It does not lie only in good works, such as those of Mother Teresa, done on the behalf of others, although it includes these. It does not lie only in philosophy or science or art, although it includes these too. It lies precisely in the awareness that all of these things are valuable, in the attempt to at least to some degree be open to all of them and to see through this comprehensive awareness some traces of how they are all intimations of an underlying whole which cannot be comprehended in any part or simplistic view.

It has been clear in this discussion that some things can be known and some not. So my final comment is, "Oh, Lord, give us the ability to discover that which can be known, the courage to accept that which cannot, and the wisdom to tell the difference".

The Bible and Evolution
The Generatings (*Toledot*) of the Heavens and the Earth When They Were Created (Bara')

Professor Millard C. Lind

Text: Genesis 2:4b: These are the *generations* of the heavens and the earth when they were *created* (RSV).

This text, written by a priest, has two incompatible words: "generations" and "created." First I will provide some remarks on the word generations and the people's story of Genesis 1-11, as modified by its incompatible word, "created"; second, how this people's concept of history challenges the hierarchical kingship concept of Egypt and Babylon; finally, the meaning of the word *generations* for the creation story, Genesis 1 and 2, again in light of its incompatible antithetical and qualifying word, "created."

1. Generations: A People's Story Of The Universe And Humanity

First then, the phrase "Generations: A People's Story Of The Universe And Humanity" (Gen. 1-11). There are two types of literary material in Genesis 1-11: the story and the genealogy.[1] The attention of the West has been upon the story. We know these stories well: creation, the fall, Cain and Abel, the flood, the covenant between God, Noah, and the animals, the confusion of tongues. Individually, these stories have been studied and compared *ad infinitum* with similar stories around the world.

In contrast to the popularity of story is *genealogy*, which is repetitive and, some would say, boring. But while the genealogy may be boring to us, to "primitive peoples" it is the main point of interest, just as it is to our priestly writer. So already, right in the middle of the creation stories, he begins his refrain. In chapter 2:4 we find "These are the generations of the heavens and the earth..." Then in chapter 5, "These are the generations of Adam. In chapter 6, "These are the generations of Noah." In chapter 10, "These are the generations of Shem." In chapter 11, "These are the generations of Terah [father of Abraham]." Finally we understand. The genealogies unite the stories; they make them *one* story of the relation of humanity to God, from creation to Abraham—and then beyond. That is the Bible's gift to humanity, the holistic story which through synagogue and church, orients the one human race to the universe and to God, from creation to modern times.

Since the publication of Alex Haley's book, *Roots,* these *generations* of scripture need no longer be boring.[2] His book is a best-seller. On the basis of modern anthropological studies in African oral cultures, Haley was able to trace his ancestors from the state of Virginia to their ancestral home in Northern Africa. The writers of Genesis 1-11 borrowed the genealogy from the pre-state culture of their own tribal ancestors, Abraham, Isaac and Jacob (Genesis 12-50). With a stroke of disciplined genius they use it to tie together the various thematic stories, by which they trace the primeval period from Abraham back to the first human couple, Adam and Eve. Because of anthropological studies undergirding Haley's novel, we know that the Biblical writers, though they do not write history, had a correct historical perspective on that story, on what unites pre-state societies—the genealogy.

Now this priestly writer makes an important leap. Like his pagan neighbors would, he uses the same word, *generations,* of the universe's beginnings that he uses of human reproduction cycles throughout Genesis 5-1 (Hebrew *toledot,* from the root *yalad,* give birth to). In Genesis 5:1 we find: "This is the book of the *generations* of Adam," and in Genesis 2 we find: "these are the *generations* of the heavens and the earth..." By the word *generations* he affirms the truth made everywhere by his pagan environment: the unity of humanity not only with itself, but also with the universe. He correctly writes that the Abraham and Sarah people had their origin first in foreign, universal humanity (cf. Deut. 26); this humanity in turn, along with plants and animals, had its origin in the physical universe. Were he living today the writer may well confuse and shock a fundamentalist congregation by proclaiming, "These are the *evolvings* of the heavens and the earth when they were *created*."

Let me simplify by quoting from the Babylonian Creation Epic (*Enuma Elish*), early second millennium BCE. It begins,

> From on high the heaven had not been named,
> Firm ground had not been called by name,
> Naught but primordial Apsu, their *begetter*,
> (And) Mummu-Tiamat, she who *bore* them all,
> Their waters commingling as a single body;...
> When no gods whatever had been brought into being,...—
> Then it was that the *gods were formed within them*—ANET:60-61,
> (my emphasis).

Then the writer names these gods, each identified with various aspects of the universe. These stories are not properly called "cosmologies," the story of the creation of the universe, but rather, "cosmogonies," the story of the birth of the gods.

This emanating, pantheistic concept of the universe and its beginnings is anathema to the worshipers of the biblical God: to Moses and the prophets, to Jesus and the apostles, to synagogue, church and mosque. And it is anathema to our priestly writer of Genesis 1-11. He is a subtle thinker. He carefully qualifies the word "generations" (toledot) by a second key word: "These are the generations of the heavens and the earth when they were *created*." He denies the pantheistic myth, but affirms the unity of life with the physical universe. It's all one story!

2. The Generations: People's History Challenges Power History

Let us move on to a second observation on this qualified word, "generations." The people's history challenges power history. This time I will compare the Genesis primeval story with the ancient *Sumerian King List*.[3] The *Sumerian List* is dated to the first part of the second millennium BCE, the traditional period of Abraham. Like the Genesis story, it divides the primeval period into pre-flood, flood, and post-flood periods. The writer begins: "When kingship was lowered from heaven, kingship was first in Eridu [the presumed first capital of pre-flood Sumer]. In Eridu, Alulim became king and ruled 28,800 years." The writer continues by tracing the movement of the antediluvian capital and the rule of their kings to five cities, closing the period with a summary: "These are five cities, eight kings ruled them for 241,000 years. Then the Flood swept over the earth." Of the post-diluvian period the writer continues, "After the flood had swept over the earth and when kingship was lowered again from heaven, kingship was first in Kish. In Kish, Ga[...]ur became king and ruled 1200 years." After listing the kings of Kish, the writer summarizes, "Twenty-three kings thus ruled it for 24,510 years, three months, and three and a half days. Then, Kish was defeated in battle.., its kingship was removed to... Uruk." And so the story goes, until the capital moves to Ur, the traditional city of Abraham.

The striking parallel of the structure of the Babylonian and Biblical narratives — pre-flood, flood and post-flood periods — is matched by an equally striking contrast. The one is a kingship structure, a political power structure. The other is a genealogical structure, an egalitarian people's structure. The Sumer presentation gives a mythologized and false picture of pre-state societies—there were no kings back then. On the other hand, the biblical genealogies, though not historical in their details, are nevertheless the way pre-state society was organized. The writer-editor made his point. The one human race, though fallen, and moving toward violence and oppression, is nevertheless responsible to and cared for by God.

This contrast between these two pre-flood documents is verified by comparison of the Genesis creation stories with the *Babylonian* and *Egyptian Creation Epics.*[4] As mere creation epics these documents are misunderstood. Fundamentally, they are political documents. Both centralize political power in their respective capital cities. For example, in the Babylonian Epic the gods elevate Marduk to kingship, and his city, Babylon, to the capital of Hammurabi's empire. After the god-king Marduk makes his acceptance speech, the gods "put the following question to [him], their firstborn: Over all that your hands have created, Who will have thy *authority*; Over the grounds which your hands have created, Who will have thy *power? Babylon...*!" All the gods shout[5].

In contrast, the biblical creation narratives end, not with the enthronement of the Jerusalem monarchy, but with the creation of the family of humanity (Adam, male and female in the divine image). There is no concept of kingship or of empire in the biblical creation story. There is an implied fall, even in the writings of this priestly editor. Humans are to rule over nature; they are not to use nature's power to rule over one another.

Kingship in Israel is never "let down from heaven." It is the result of the rebellious demand of tribal elders. I repeat, while the story of humanity in the *Sumerian King List* is a political power history, united by kingship, the biblical story is a people's history, united by their generations. In one awful struggle that concept is extended throughout the entire Bible to the birth and ministry of Jesus of Nazareth and the coming of the Holy Spirit at Pentecost.

3. Creation: An Enabling Story Prompted By Divine Word

My third and final observation is that the creation story is an *enabling* story prompted by the divine word. With an emphasis on the priestly writer's qualifying term, we read: "These are the generations of the heaven and the earth *when they were created*." Unlike the noun *generations* (toledot, from the verbal root yalad, to give birth, cf. Gen. 4:1), the noun and verb "Creator," and created are used in the Bible exclusively in reference to God and divine activity. As verb, this occurs six times in the first creation story. Though the two creation stories are quite different in their literary structures and vocabulary (Gen. 1:1-2:4a; 2:4b-25), both support the concept of a transcendent, personal God who precedes the creation and is nowhere confused with the divinely created work.

From the perspective of biblical faith, the most important instrument of creation is the word of God: "And God said." Just as the phrase "these are the generations" unites the primeval history, so "and God said" is the repeated phrase throughout the first creation story. This corresponds to the prophetic emphasis throughout the Bible: The call of God to Abram (Gen.12:1), to Moses (Exod. 4:7). Even in the book of Kings, the king is not the king by his army and police power, but the word of God through the prophet determines history. In 2 Kings 17:24 we read: "Yet the Lord warned Israel and Judah by every prophet... saying, 'Turn from your evil ways and keep my commandments... in accordance with all the law... which I sent you by my servants the prophets.'..." This creation by the Word is celebrated in the Gospel of John, which begins as Genesis 1: "*In the beginning* was the Word... It was in the beginning with God; all things were made through him... And the Word became flesh and dwelt among us ..." This concept may have dialogical possibilities with the science writer of the *New York Times*, who, in the July, 2001 issue, speaks of "the universe's cosmological DNA."[6] Like Genesis 1, the Gospel's transcendent *Word* is creator of the universe and, in Israel's prophetic history, becomes immanent in the human story.

Although our priestly writer rejects the concept of the universe as the emanation of divinity, he nevertheless supports the ancient Near Eastern concept that the universe possesses within itself certain divinely given, generative qualities and powers of development. The Creator enables:

> And God said, Let the *earth bring forth* vegetation... The *earth brought forth* vegetation (Gen. 1:11-12).
> And God said, Let the *waters bring forth* swarms of living creatures... (1:20).
> And God said, Let the *earth bring forth* living creatures... (1:24).

Just as God is the divine enabler who blesses humanity so that humanity can procreate and rule the earth (1:16-18), so God enables sun and moon as greater and lesser lights to rule over day and night (Gen. 1:16-18), and so God enables earth and waters to "bring forth" (cf. Gen. 1:22). This enabling of the waters and earth to "bring forth" is not contrasted with, but is parallel to God's creative act, as if in cooperation: "So *God created* the great sea monsters[7] and every living creature... "(1:21; cf. 1:25).

Again our writer is subtle. In his choice of the Hebrew word translated "bring forth," he never uses the technical Hebrew word of a mother giving birth to a child (yalad, the root of toledot), but uses more general terms, such as *yasa'*, "to go out" (Gen. 1:12, 24, hiph'il). This word, used occasionally for giving birth, is used more generally of the animals when they go out of the ark (8:19) and, more significantly, of Yahweh's bringing Israel out of Egypt, and in the perspective from which the writer views creation: "I am Yahweh your God *who brought you out* of the land of Egypt, out of the house of slavery" (Exod. 20:2).

Although this creation story uses the word "created" only of God's activity, I express carefully what I think is his important point. By the creative enabling word of God, the heavens and the earth become partners with divinity in creation. To some extent this is comparable to humanity, which is, by the enabling blessing of God, to become fruitful, fill and rule the earth (cf. Gen. 1:28).

So, the writer's qualified concept of the earth bringing forth (Gen. 1) is parallel to that of his qualified *generations* of our text: these are the generations... when they were *created*" Gen. 2:4). If this observation is correct, it has tremendous possibilities for drawing a parallel between the biblical creation story and a "demythologized"[8] Twenty-first-century evolutionary narrative. The ever-present personal and transcendent God creates each item of the universe not in isolation, but as Creator blesses and enables; and over the eons God unites the farthest Gamma-Ray Burster with the most recently born child. Since many members of the modern scientific community have corrected their misconceived presuppositions of Newtonian science,[9] it is time for biblical scholars to correct their own mistaken reading of the biblical text, and to make this new reading a part of the religion-science dialogue.

I close with a summary of my three observations on the *evolvings* of the heavens and the earth when they were *created*: 1) The generations or demythologized evolvings of the heaven and the earth is *one unified story* with its successive generations of humanity; 2) The biblical concept of a genealogical *people's structure* of creation and history challenges the Near East concept of a kingship *power structure* of creation and history; and 3) The creating Word of God, the "cosmological DNA," enables and enlists the physical universe and humanity as partners in creation and history.[10]

Discussions

The principal part of the conference consisted of discussions with Professor Ellis on the topics raised in his public and private lectures, as well as topics arising naturally in the discussions themselves. There were four separate discussion sessions. The first of these was an open microphone discussion after the Friday evening lecture. The second took place Saturday morning before the second public lecture. The third was late Saturday afternoon. The fourth followed the internal lecture on Sunday morning.

Many topics were revisited during the discussions with an increased depth. Therefore, the discussions have been rearranged here based on the general topics considered. In his first lecture, Professor Ellis presented four worlds into which he divided the topics he discussed. This provided the natural basis for an outline. Indeed all topics could, perhaps, have been made to fit this general four-part outline, but because such issues as kenosis and God's action naturally attract attention as separate topics, they were treated as such.

Some editorial liberty was taken with the comments and questions of the conference participants. Every effort was made to adhere to the intent of the individual speaker, as I understood that. But comments were often shortened and sometimes dropped. Professor Ellis' responses, however, appear essentially verbatim. Certain comments have been removed on consultation with Professor Ellis. All personal comments have been edited out.

As explained in the editor's preface, a speaker number indicates the identity of the person raising a question or providing a comment, except in the Friday evening session. Professor Ellis is designated by name (George Ellis). Both of these are given in bold-font.

Effort was also made to keep the references to authors and texts mentioned in the questions and comments. The editor takes full responsibility for all errors in these. A table of contents for this section follows.

Discussions

World 1: Matter and Forces
Chaos
Modular Systems
Top-Down Causality
Fine Tuning and Multiple Universes
Quantum Indeterminacy
Conciliance and Reductionism

World 2: Consciousness
Spiritual Reality
Consciousness and Causality
Mind and Body

World 3: Aristotelian World
Hierarchy, Evolution and God's Direction
Biology and Genetic Determinism
Ethics

World 4: Platonic World
Mathematics and Physical Laws
Mathematical Reality

Hierarchy and the 4 Worlds
Status of the Equations

Aesthetics
Aesthetics and the Search for God
Aesthetics and Relationships

Kenosis
Discussions Among Religions
Biological Evolution
Fundamentalism
International Conflict
Politics
Psychology, Sociobiology, and Human Communities
Ethics

God's Action
Scholars Involved
God's Action, the Laws of Physics and Kenosis
God and Higher Dimensions
God's Interaction and Prayer
God's Interaction and Free Will

Matter and Forces

Chaos
Modular Systems
Top-Down Causality
Fine Tuning and Multiple Universes
Quantum Indeterminacy
Conciliance and Reductionism

Chaos

[Friday Evening]

Question: Is there such a thing as chaos?

George Ellis: Yes. Early on I talked about physical laws. One of the things we have discovered recently is that even totally deterministic physical laws can lead to unpredictable results. Incredibly small differences in initial conditions for a system can lead to exponentially diverse results. And the future of such a system is impossible to predict, even though it is deterministic. For example the equations for the predictions of weather are completely determinate. But even if we could get all the information we cannot predict the weather in the long term because the states diverge quite rapidly. So no matter how good your prediction in the end it will not match reality.

A really important question to ask is whether this has anything to do with the origin and the evolution of life? There are some people who believe that it could be important to the evolution of life. Personally I believe that it is not. This is because the human body and all living beings are complexly constructed feedback systems in with an incredible number of feedback loops, which are designed to damp any disturbance, and whenever you have an effective feedback system chaos does not happen.

As an example of a system that is constructed in a way that promotes chaotic behavior, consider a billiard table in which the cushions are not straight. The cushions are slightly convex towards the inside. On such a table the angle between the path of the billiard ball toward the cushion and the reflection is amplified. Within about ten bounces on a billiard table with slightly bent walls it is impossible to predict where the billiard ball will be even though it is a totally deterministic system. This is a chaotic system. But in a well-engineered system this will not happen. In an aircraft with automatic pilot, for instance, there are feedback-loops built in that counteract any deviation from the selected course. So some physical systems are chaotic but many are not.

Question: So you are defining chaos as a state of absolute unpredictability and you say that such a state does exist.

George Ellis: Yes.

Question: But the reason we are not able to make that determination is not a limitation of our measurement devices or our mathematical formulas. Rather it is a result of the fact that there is a state of reality that exists that is totally beyond any mathematical or physical description. Do you see where I am headed?

George Ellis: Sorry I should have made that clearer. The reason you cannot is because you can only measure the initial position and velocity to a finite accuracy. There is always an error. So in any system there is always some deviation between prediction and observation. In a chaotic system, however, that error will become so large as to make the prediction completely unreliable.

In this context I should mention quantum uncertainty. At the micro-level there is a very strange feature known as quantum uncertainty. It is impossible to measure both the position and the velocity of a particle. This is built into the foundation of the microphysics. For example say you have a very small particle and wish to measure its position. You have to do so by using some other particle. A photon, a particle of light, can be used to measure where the particle is. In the process that photon smashes into the particle and exchanges momentum giving that particle a velocity. And so you don't know where it is moving to, even though you measured its position. That is, at the fundamental level there is a complete inability to measure exactly the state of physical systems.

Modular Systems

[Friday Evening]

Question: I was interested in your analogy of top-down design [causality]. Is there another way to look at this? I am thinking about Marvin Minsky's idea of non-intelligent agents and intelligence coming as a result of the interaction. Is that what you are considering? Particularly I am thinking about the idea that there are smaller independent units and it is the interaction of those units that is important. And then is there a limit to this top-down causality?

George Ellis: Basically the whole point of modularity is that you can build up an incredibly complex system out of simple modules. For example, chemistry emerges from physics and biochemistry from chemistry and so on. In order for that to succeed you need to obey certain various principles of abstraction. Levels of extreme complexity then emerge. Consciousness is an emergent property. There is no question about that and presumably it is by interactions of modules of a sufficient number of sufficiently complex modules which I think is what you are saying.

Fine Tuning and Multiple Universes
[Friday Evening]

Speaker 1: Scientific materialists escape from the concept that there is a creator who made a choice at the beginning by introducing the multiple universes. When people take that position are they not implicitly accepting the existence of your third world – that is Aristotle's landscape of possibilities?

George Ellis: I would see this slightly differently. I think physicists always have in mind that world of possibilities, but they do not express it that way. They express it in terms of the existence of the laws of physics. The laws of physics are what describe that landscape, at least for physicists. Biologists talk more directly about a possibility landscape. So I think they accept it as well, although they also phrase it slightly differently. I phrased it the way I did in order to avoid getting into the question of the ontology of the laws of physics, which is a very deep and unanswered question. Now, in terms of the multiverses something very interesting arises. Martin Rees[1] has written a couple of books about this, as have various others. People like Martin Rees realize fully that there is this very fine-tuned nature of the universe that allows life to exist. I will be saying a little more about that today [Saturday]. In order to avoid the implication of design and to use the physicist's concept of statistical physics and probability, they imagine an ensemble of universes, which likely are called the multiverse.

There are various different ways in which this ensemble can be realized. One way is something called chaotic inflation, in which our universe, beyond the horizon (the limit of observation), is quite different from what it is inside the horizon. Way out there where we cannot see the universe or have any direct contact with it, everything is totally different. There is another concept, which Martin (Rees) defends by what he calls the slippery slope argument. This argument considers that there exist a number of totally disconnected universes. In fact he even talks about an infinite number of such totally disconnected universes. I think that is very loose talk because infinity is a very difficult concept. In any case, the Martin Rees hypothesis, which Max Tegmark and various people have talked about, considers that there is an ensemble of universes that they call the multiverse.

Now, firstly, I regard this as metaphysics rather than physics. You will never be able to prove that this is correct. You will never prove it is correct because you have no causal connection. So I think it is quite clear it is metaphysics not physics. The second point is that they seem to think that there is only one such multiverse. But when you think about it the concept is not actually well defined. There can be many different kinds of multiverses. And then you run into all sorts of problems regarding trying to deal with the statistical properties of an infinite ensemble and so on. And you can get any answer you want by varying it [the ensemble]. But suppose that you forget about these two problems. Then the question reverts to the original one simply moved back one step. So the real question is, "Why does the multiverse exist, and why does it have the properties it does?" But this is actually just a way of deferring the problem.

Speaker 1: There is the time-honored principle of scientific reasoning called Ockham's Razor. Is this being ignored?.

George Ellis: Well, this is a matter of debate. Someone like Paul Davies would agree with you completely and has said so, whereas someone like Martin Rees may say that the idea of a multiverse is just one simple concept. The response from people like Paul Davies and myself is to say that this totally violates Ockham's Razor, because in order to explain the one universe that you know exists you suppose an infinite ensemble of universes, which you cannot prove exist. That is the opposite of Ockham's Razor, but one is in a philosophical debate here, since Martin may claim that the idea of an ensemble is a simple concept.

Quantum Indeterminacy

[Saturday Morning]

Speaker 3: You said that the concept of quantum indeterminacy could be used to explain God's interaction with the world. Is this threatened by the possibility of a deterministic explanation such as David Bohm has attempted?

George Ellis: There are several points [to be noted] about this. The first point is that quantum indeterminacy, from the physical viewpoint, is really taken as a dogma nowadays, except by the Bohmians. I will return to that in a minute. The standard dogma is that quantum uncertainty has an ontological status. It is irreducible and irremediable. But there is a whole class of hidden variable theories, which is being tested, and the tests are showing that a hidden variable theory cannot work unless it is non-local. My response to that, if I were to pursue it, would be to say, "Well, fine. I am prepared to think of God as a hidden variable, or at least of God's influence as a hidden variable, which is not local." There is no conflict with any of these hidden variable theories.

Now the Bohmian position is to say that quantum mechanics is actually deterministic because there is this pilot-wave which guides it and so on. But to me that is a sleight-of-hand because you're saying it [quantum mechanics] is deterministic but the outcome is not predictable. So I haven't spent a lot of time looking into it [Bohmian quantum theory] because in the end it seems to me to be a theory that doesn't actually gain you anything. The results of quantum mechanics remain indeterminate.

Now it would be interesting if Bohm's theory enabled you to predict things, which it does not. There is, however, something that I think is quite interesting. Consider for a moment the double-slit experiment with photons. Photons come from a source, pass through one or the other of two slits, and then strike a screen. You claim that you cannot tell where the next photon is going to be. Now suppose that you take the positions at which all the photons strike the screen and use those to generate a sequence of numbers. Your problem is to prove that this sequence of numbers is random. But there is a theorem that says you cannot prove that. You cannot prove that any sequence of numbers is random. All you can say is you have not detected an algorithm which generates that sequence. For example, if I give you a fraction of the middle of pi and ask you whether it is a random sequence or not, you are going to say it's random because you don't know it's a bit of the middle of pi. But someone clever enough will find out that it is not random. There is a possibility, and this is just a possibility, that quantum processes are not random. Then there is possibly some underlying principle that determines where the photons go, but people just have not found the algorithm yet. This is a philosophical point. I am not putting it forward as a serious physical theory, but I am saying it would be interesting to try to use modern pattern-detection techniques to see if you could find an algorithm for constructing the pattern. It is just conceivable that there is one. If there is such an algorithm our understanding of quantum mechanics will be totally changed.

Conciliance and Reductionism

[Sunday]

Speaker 20: Do you consider your views of conciliance to be different from those of E. O. Wilson?

George Ellis: Wilson is obtaining conciliance by reductionism. I just read a very interesting review of a conference with proceedings published in the Annals of the New York Academy of Sciences. The conference was on the unity of science with E. O. Wilson as one of the key speakers. The review made it absolutely clear that what he's putting forward is reductionism as a way of obtaining conciliance. He wants to reduce the social sciences and then he wants to reduce ethics to social sciences. And so, whatever he calls it, he's actually promoting reductionism and calling it conciliance. I have read his book, but that was a number of years ago.

Spiritual Reality
Consciousness and Causality
Mind and Body

Spiritual Reality

[Friday Evening]

Question: Religion uses terms like "spiritual world" and "spiritual reality." How do those terms fit into the scheme that you outlined?

George Ellis: That is what I will be picking up tomorrow [This answer was given on Friday evening]. What I have been trying to do this evening is lay the groundwork into which the adding of the idea of a spiritual world is much less of a step. If you just have a world of matter and particles, and that is all that you are acknowledging, then introducing a spiritual world is something totally different and alien. If you have the four worlds that I have described, and I claim that all physicists will eventually have to admit the existence of these four worlds, then including a spiritual world is not alien.

Consciousness and Causality
[Saturday Morning]

Speaker 2: Could you discuss the basic elements of the conscious world? What are they? What is the logic of the conscious world? How do you structure that world? And then in particular how does that world relate to the physical matter world?

George Ellis: I want to be agnostic about quite a few of the issues you raise. I claim that you cannot have a causally complete system without including in that the world of consciousness. And then the obvious fundamental point, which we all realize, is that scientifically we do not understand consciousness. We haven't even begun to understand consciousness. This is what David Chalmers[2] has called the hard problem. We know lots about perception, we know lots about neurons, and so on, but we do not know how this thing is integrated and how we get the perception, the qualia, of the colors and all the rest of it.

Nevertheless, let us consider the world of consciousness from a causal viewpoint. Firstly there is the logical part of it, the ideas, the theories, and the concepts. Those are causally affective. For instance if I am designing a jumbo jet, I design it on the basis of a logical kind of pattern, and that pattern gets implemented and turned into real nuts and bolts and so on. So those plans are causally effective. They are causally effective because of the second part, which is intentions and emotions. Someone has made the decision that it is going to happen because they want it to happen. So it is a question of conscious choices and decisions, and those decisions are effective. I add emotions because emotions determine what one chooses. Therefore emotions do effect what happens in the real world.

The third component I identified is that of the consciously constructed social constructions. The laws governing society constitute an example of this. The whole of law is socially, consciously constructed and it has real physical consequences. I gave the example yesterday of the death penalty. If you have a death penalty, then sitting somewhere in the state is the apparatus to carry out that death penalty. That apparatus is the physical realization of those laws. So I don't have to get involved in the incredible intricacies of how thoughts do manage to cause electrons to flow in your arms. For my purposes here I just have to say that we know they do and if you don't take that into account you have got a causally incomplete description of the universe.

Speaker 1: And that describes the relationship in World 2 and World 1. But you didn't talk at all about World 1 affecting World 2.

George Ellis: Clearly thoughts supervene on the brain. But the point I made was that a thought or an idea is not just related to those brain impulses, because it gets translated into digital form, into printed form, and so on. And so the thought in some sense exists in an abstract world. In mathematical terms it is an equivalence relation of a whole mass of representations. And given a specific thought you can represent it in sound, you can represent it in print, you can represent it electronically and so on, and so on. So it is quite clear that the thought itself is separate from any one of those representations.

Speaker 1: It has a separate ontological status?

George Ellis: It has a separate ontological status, yes.

Mind and Body
[Saturday Morning]

Speaker 11: There is a lot of popular discussion, particularly with respect to medical situations, of a mind-body interaction. There is evidence that the mind, or the emotional state of a person, may affect the immune system. Are you aware of any robust evidence of a mind-body interaction, particularly in a physiological sense?

George Ellis: Firstly I am a total amateur in this area and am happy to be corrected. But I will make a couple of comments. A particular book, which I have looked at and has really impressed me, is Esther Sternberg's book

The Balance Within.[3] This deals in great detail with how the immune system can be affected by the mind.

I have come to what I admit is an amateur position. There are two instances that really interest me. One is that my old colleague, Stephen Hawking, who ought to have died twenty years ago, continues to live. In my opinion this is simply because of his will power. He has decided to live and he is alive because of that. There is a converse to that. I am very aware that there are some people who decide that they are going to die and they die. For instance people in sickbeds may stay alive until some relative comes and visits them, and then the following day or two they just die. I can see no other explanation for this than the top-down action of the mind on their very existence.

Finally let me also mention another instance. I know of a hospital where there were many starving children and many orphans. In that hospital there was a ward in which there were infants who had been abandoned by their parents. The ward sisters used to go bustling around feeding the infants as well as the others. Although they had been given every physical requirement, many of them failed to gain weight, and, in fact were gradually dying. Then one person set up what she called the sunshine ward. The difference between the sunshine ward and all the other wards was that in the sunshine ward the people came in and played with the children. They talked to the children and responded to them. And those children gained weight because of that mental interaction.

Hierarchy, Evolution and God's Direction
Biology and Genetic Determinism
Ethics

Hierarchy, Evolution and God's Direction

[Friday Evening]

Question: Are there limits on either end of the hierarchy you have proposed? Might there be something on above the hierarchy and something actually far below. Looking at the upper end of the hierarchy I would like to hear you comment on some of the recent things we have heard in the press about intelligent design. How does that fit into the hierarchy as you see it? Or does it?

George Ellis: These are two separate questions. At the upper end of the hierarchy on the physical side you have got cosmology. Because the

97

cosmos is the largest physical system there is, I am going to make the case tomorrow that you can only understand cosmology by adding a metaphysical layer. That is a layer that is not comprehended by physics. At the top level of the human side of the hierarchy you have ethics. I will make the case tomorrow that if there is anything to ethics it is theology.

At the bottom of the hierarchy you again run into metaphysics. You see our ability to experiment comes to an end both at the bottom and at the top level. At the top it comes to a limit because of horizons in cosmology that I mentioned. We cannot observe the universe on a bigger scale than the horizon. We will never ever know what lies outside the horizon. At the bottom scale our ability to interact with this is limited by the size of particle detectors that we can make. There is a limit to the energies we can attain. This limits the lowest scales we can get to. We are never ever going to be able to get to the bottom of the hierarchy because we are never ever going to be able to do the experiment. We are going to be able to make theories about it and that is where the theories of quantum gravity come in. These theories are an active area of research at the present time, but testing them is going to be extraordinarily difficult.

The separate question was about intelligent design. I accept evolutionary theory. I am, of course, aware that there is a counter movement that does not accept that. There are also some problems with evolutionary theory. The first problem is that evolutionary biology is not an experimental science; it is a historical science. And all historical sciences are always going to be subject to doubt simply because they are historical. You can't re-run evolution and see what will happen. That is the first reason for which uncertainty will remain.

Another problem with the standard theory relates to the time involved, which is a result of the possibility space. I talked about the possibility space, but what I didn't say is how unbelievably large that possibility space is for biological action. Consider a change of one hundred molecules in an organic peptide and ask for the number of possible organic molecules that may result. For a chain of about a hundred molecules in a complex organic molecule the possibility of space is about ten to the hundred twenty molecules. That is an immense number.

Now the phrase "immense number" is very carefully thought out. An astronomical number is ten to the eighty, which is the number of protons in the visible universe. The number of possible chemical combinations for this organic molecule is forty orders of magnitude more.

It is much, much more than an astronomical number. There is, therefore, no way that the standard evolutionary process could, in the time available, have explored all the possibilities. Evolution could only have explored a subset of possibilities because there simply isn't the time for it to explore that immense set of possibilities. This is what people like Fred Hoyle have understood. Unless there is some guidance of the path of evolution, you can't get to where we are.

This is well understood in the microbiology community, and this is what has led to the theory of autocatalytic hypercycles, which Eigen and other people have been putting forward. Basically, you have cycles of cycles which are autocatalytic. This is the concept of complexity for explaining how we got to where we are in the allotted time, and I think this probably works. But then this, like all theories, raises the question of how the fundamental laws of physics incorporate into its structure such a hypercycle that will lead to intelligence. And when you think about it that then becomes the really mysterious issue.

Burt, you asked specifically if there is divine intelligence guiding evolution. Here you're in very controversial territory. I have to say that if you believe in a divine being in the standard kind of way there are two ways in which this could happen. The first is that the divine being decides, as the person who keeps the laws of physics in order, that he or she for the moment will suspend or alter the laws of physics in order to obtain a certain effect. Now most people don't like that idea, and certainly for scientists this is a completely unacceptable position.

The second one, which is being explored by various people, including Bob Russell[4] of CTNS,[5] uses quantum uncertainty. This is the fundamental uncertainty of the microscopic state. Physicists cannot tell you the result of microscopic interactions. They can only tell you of the probability. For example, if you fire a particle such as an electron through a very thin slit toward a screen, it is impossible for a physicist to tell you where on the screen it will strike. The physicist can give you the statistical law but cannot tell you the particular position where it will end up. Another example is a radioactive atom. An atom in an excited state is sitting there. It is unstable and it's going to decay. There is no known way of saying when it will decay. You know statistically how a collection of such atoms will decay. But you can say nothing about the individual. Now if you want to, you can say that a divine being is in control of this uncertainty. It's uncertain to human beings, but it's completely controlled by the divine creator.

You can, if you wish, claim that God is immanent everywhere and is holding the laws of physics in existence. There is then no reason that you could not make the claim that God is in control of whatever happens and certainly can make the result whatever He or She wants it to be. That means that God could then slightly tweak the DNA at various points in order to obtain the desired result. In this picture one single change is caused in one single atom through a single photon or cosmic ray, which may then change the course of evolutionary history. Well, if you want to you can make the claim that God chooses to slightly tweak those quantum uncertainties, making the outcome one thing rather than the other. No scientist will be able to prove that you are wrong. But you will never be able to prove that you are right.

Question: Does that mean that there is some bottom-up causality that constrains the will of God? That is, because the statistics will have to come out the way they do, God can't fiddle as He chooses.

George Ellis: No God would have to obey the statistics, but of course you then come across a fundamental point about statistics. You can never violate a statistical law. All you can do is get a probability, which may be very small, but all that the physical statistical law says is that it's improbable. So you are absolutely right. If that kind of intervention were to take place it would have to be done in such a way as to broadly maintain the statistics.

Biology and Genetic Determinism
[Saturday Afternoon]

Speaker 12: Could you elaborate on your views on the biological aspects of morality, and what do you have to say about the research indicating neurological differences in individuals with Antisocial Personality Disorder, who have no conscience? Can you speak specifically to that?

George Ellis: There is an increasing literature that recognizes that the way that the human genome works out in practice is strongly correlated to the environment within which the genome is interpreted. There is absolutely no mechanical process at work.

The single most important thing that has come out of the human genome project is the statement that, in spite of the incredible amount of information in the CGAT[6] coding at the digital level in a DNA molecule, there are only forty thousand genes in the human genome. Now, that means that the entire human body, including the brain, has to be shaped by those forty thousand genes. What is the problem? The problem is that in the brain there are ten to the eleventh neurons. At most, half of those forty thousand genes can be available for the brain, because the rest of them have to fix up the heart and the feet, and the lungs, and so on. So you have got twenty thousand genes to specify ten to the eleventh neurons. There is not a mechanism available whereby information from that incredibly small number of genes could do any seriously detailed wiring of the brain. There is not a fraction of the information necessary for that detailed interconnectedness of the neurons. Many of the theories, which claim that the DNA determines specific modules in the brain, are fantasy.

There is, furthermore, an incredibly weak link on the other side. You have to ask yourself how you would feed into the DNA the information for a specific wiring of the brain. The fundamental dogma of modern theoretical biology is that the genes you pass on to your child are unchanged by anything you do or learn. Your genes were fixed before you ever learned anything. Therefore that supposed causal link between behavior and your genes does not exist, because there's no mechanism. So I think there's a double-fold bind there for people who claim a serious link between genes and behavior. I think that genes can only determine the broadest patterns of behavior, but not any detailed patterns of behavior.

I would be a little cautious with the phrase "people who have no conscience," but let's accept that. Yes, it will be in your brain, but it will be in your brain because your brain has developed in a certain way, not because it was in the gene. I think that is really quite crucial. And there is a lot of literature recognizing this very strong environmental effect. This is, of course, one of the very old questions regarding human life. How much is hereditary and how much is environment? But if you just think about this, about those twenty thousand genes you've got available, it is a fraction of the information you need to produce any serious wiring of the brain to give you certain response patterns. That limitation is really a problem.

Of course if there is physical damage to the brain, it could affect your morality. There is a coding of your basic moral stance in your brain. In a sense that's a point that Nancey [Murphy] and I made. The question is whether this encoding comes from the heredity side or the environment and the way you interact with the environment. I am saying that if you just look at the information and the figures, it has to come, in the main, from your interaction with the environment rather than from a heredity component.

Speaker 1: There was a study conducted at Argonne National Laboratory in which such things as hair samples, blood samples, were collected from prisoners in the Illinois prison system, including some on death row and some posthumously. Interesting correlations were found between strongly sociopathic behavior and ratios of certain chemical elements, among other things. Changes in body chemistry were correlated substantially with antisocial behavior. This is, of course, what you would call an environmental effect rather than a genetic effect, since this chemistry would come to your body through the intake of various things.

George Ellis: Let me comment on development. Given what I've just said, you can ask how does the brain shape itself? How does it get this amazing ability? And the answer is largely given in a book by Gerald M. Edelman entitled *Neural Darwinism.*[7] The brain shapes itself based on a kind of Darwinian process in which it sets up certain connections absolutely randomly. There is an extraordinary way in which, as the brain develops, neurons send out dendrites, which just link in whatever they link in. But then some of those linkages get reinforced, and some die away, according to a feedback mechanism, which is basically a Darwinian one. The question is which of these connections are good ones and should be kept, or are bad ones? Emotions control that. You experience certain things, and the emotions basically tell the brain, this is a good connection and we want to keep it, or this is a bad one, and we want it to die away. There's a tremendous amount of research going on at the moment about the way in which a certain series of fundamental emotions sets up the choices of what you're going to keep. It is perfectly possible that through that process you could, in fact, create an individual who would be extremely antagonistic and hostile. This would result if the link from the negative emotions were stronger than that from positive ones, which is possible. One important author investigating this is Antonio Damasio,[8] who has pointed out that one must not talk about intellect free of emotions.

Speaker 9: As you were talking about the huge number of brain cells it struck me that there is a similar problem in the body. We have one hundred trillion cells in the body, which all collaborate, but in a way dependent on where they are in the body. A deterministic control by the DNA doesn't make sense in that situation. The information needed to do it may be there. But how is that turned on in one way in one cell, and in a different way in a different cell?

George Ellis: I'm not an expert in this area, but I have read quite widely in it, and I've talked with Lewis Wolpert, who is one of the leading experts in the area of developmental biology. He spoke, very positively, about positional information. There is a very large body of data, which is getting more and more precise, about morphogens. Morphogens are diffusible molecules secreted by a signaling center. This diffusion sets up morphogen concentration gradients, which affect cellular differentiation. There are chains in which some morphogens then trigger others. A particular case that's been looked at in great detail is the segmentation of the fruit fly. Wolpert claims that through this process of positional information the problem is basically solved, and all that's required is a few details. I have talked with other people in the area, and I simply don't believe that it is basically solved. I think that [positional information] is a major part of it. However, if we consider the inner ear, we notice that there is this extraordinarily intricate mechanism of bones, and I cannot see how you get the fine sculpting of those cells out of this mechanism. I certainly don't say it's impossible. The mechanism of positional information can set up the broad structures and the broad bases, but it still seems to me that there is a major question about the very, very fine detailing. As I have said you've only got these forty thousand genes and some structures are very, very precisely defined. The visual path is another example of a very precisely defined circuit from the photoreceptors to the brain.

Ethics

[Sunday]

Speaker 19: How does one separate religion and ethics? The Decalogue defines God as one who delivers from a state of slavery: "I am the Lord your God, who brought you out of the land of Egypt, out of the house of bondage." That is, God is defined in terms of what we call social ethics, or political ethics.

George Ellis: I cannot answer that one. My comment is simply that if you look at the Science and Religion debate you find a huge amount of discussion on evolution and the big bang, and similar questions considered purely as scientific issues, and then a separate debate on bioethics, cloning, and so on. But they normally aren't brought together into an integrated whole.

Platonic World

Mathematics and Physical Laws
Mathematical Reality
Hierarchy and the 4 Worlds
Status of the Equations

Mathematics and Physical Laws

[Friday Evening]

Question: One of the four worlds you mentioned is the mathematical world. What is the relationship between the mathematical world and the physical world, which you called World 3?

George Ellis: The relation between the mathematical and the physical world is a fundamentally difficult question. The question is the relationship between mathematics and the physical laws. There have been many papers written on the unreasonable effectiveness of mathematics in describing

the physical world. There are basically two options. The one option is
that somewhere in an abstract world there are, in some sense or other,
mathematically based laws. And all protons, all neutrons, all electrons,
[and all elementary particles] then are constructed to obey those
mathematical laws. That is, it is possible that the laws of physics are
really mathematical and that the physical world simply must obey
those laws. The other option is that physical things have certain
behaviors and we have just found that mathematics happens to describe
those behaviors very well.

So the mathematical laws may be prescriptive or they may be
descriptive. There are problems both ways. If the laws really are
mathematical then how do they come into being? Here we are really
speaking about a Platonic point of view. This means that there is a world
of mathematical laws, which has a rigid control on the physical world,
and I think that is the way many physicists actually think.

It is quite an extraordinary thing that mathematics is so successful.
But there are still unanswered questions. Why are neutrons and protons
the same everywhere in the universe? And why are these properties the
same as they were at the beginning? What is the ontological status of
matter? I'm struggling for words for a very difficult kind of area in which
there is absolutely no resolution.

Question: Maybe we will never know what the ultimate way of describing
reality and nature is, but mathematics happens to be the best
approximation that we have been able to come up with as a language for
describing it. But this doesn't have the ontological status that you've
proposed.

George Ellis: I accept that and I think that this is the position of many of
my more thoughtful colleagues like Bill Stoeger.[9] I suspect, however,
that most physicists believe Maxwell's Equations prescribe rather than
describe.

Question: World 4, the Platonic World, is open-ended. We have no idea
what we will discover in the next thousand years. It seems to me that
this open-ended nature must be incorporated into our thinking of the
other three worlds.

George Ellis: What I hear you saying is that we only know a bit of this fourth world and are never going to know all of it. There are other difficult aspects to this that I did not mention. Just as there is quantum uncertainty at the foundation of physics, there is also uncertainty at the foundation of mathematics. I refer here to Gödel's incompleteness theorem. The illusion people once had that mathematics was going to be this perfect deterministic structure that we could sort out and understand has been totally destroyed. This does not mean that mathematics is necessarily uncertain or indeterminate. It means that our understanding of it is going to be uncertain.

Mathematical Reality

[Saturday Morning]

Speaker 4: If mathematics is a reality I would expect a contradiction-free and consistent system. I believe [David] Hilbert tried to prove that you can have a complete system derivable from its own axioms, but then Kurt Gödel established the incompleteness theorem. What kind of proof do we have that mathematics is in fact a reality? How do you get around Gödel's logical incompleteness theorem?

George Ellis: My answer is a little like my answer about the brain. I'm not offering a theory of how thoughts create action. I have thought about this and I am willing to talk about it, but I'm not offering that as part of my theory. In the same sense, I am not claiming any position on the logical completeness or underlying axioms of mathematics because I don't know how that works. But what I am saying is that the world of mathematics firstly is discovered, not invented. At least part of it is.

Let me be a little bit cautious here. There are some branches of mathematics that one could say are invented rather than discovered. But there are many parts of mathematics which, it's quite clear to me, are discovered rather than invented. Examples are the value of pi, the square root of two, the existence of irrational numbers, and so on. These were not invented. In fact they were discovered to the dismay of mathematicians. Mathematicians didn't want to discover irrational numbers. But in a sense that is the hallmark of something which people haven't invented. They didn't want to find it.

Such things are causally effective in the following very simple way. I can print out the number pi. There are then marks on paper that are a representation of that number. In fact if the number were different, those marks would be different. Yesterday I showed you the Mandelbrot and Julia sets on the screen. Those were physical representations. In those representations electrons striking the screen made certain parts of the screen glow. So the mathematical equation has resulted in a specific pattern, which is realized physically. In that sense it is causally effective.

But there is one thing I didn't make clear. I want to step back a minute to the nature of the world of the consciousness: the thoughts, and so on. There is one really important point, which I should have mentioned, but did not. Thoughts cover all sorts of things that may or may not exist. We can have a thought of an elephant, and we can describe that idea in many different ways, in pictorial form and digital form and so on. We can also have a thought of a fairy or of a unicorn. That is we can have thoughts of things that don't exist. I must make absolutely clear my position on this. The thought of the fairy is real. I can prove this thought is real because I can show you a picture of a fairy in a book. That means the thought of a fairy is real. But that does not mean that fairies exist. The World 2 is the world of consciousness. The whole of epistemology deals with the question "How does World 2, that world of thoughts, relate to World 1, the world of things?" In the case of elephants, there is a tick [a check mark]. The concept of an elephant does correspond to a physical thing that exists. In the case of a unicorn there is a cross [an x mark]. The concept of the unicorn does not correspond to a physical thing. But it is very important to realize that the concept of the unicorn exists and is causally effective. The concept of a unicorn, a fairy, an elephant, and so on, are all causally effective because I can show you in a dictionary or in a fairy tale that the representation of this is written down on the paper and it exists in print and so on. Thoughts can be causally effective even if they refer to objects that do not exist, and epistemology is precisely the question about which thoughts correspond to things that do exist and which thoughts correspond to things that don't exist. I should have made that clear.

Speaker 5: What is the implication of considering that mathematics discovers things versus mathematics invents things. What is the implication of that for our weekend [this conference]?

George Ellis: I suppose that the way to put it is to say that the axioms are invented and then the implications are discovered. But what I really want to say is that at least some parts of mathematics are discovered. I have used as examples the base of the natural logarithms, *e*, the square root of two, the number pi, and the Mandelbrot set. Those are examples of mathematics that are discovered rather than invented. The implication is that there is this platonic world [of Forms]. We don't know how it exists, but we know *that* it exists precisely because we can investigate it and discover these relations. The way we express the result of our investigation will depend on the language we use. If we express pi in a decimal system it will look different than if we express it in the binary system. But the value of the number pi is something that we discover. And we are convinced that a physicist on Alpha-Centuri or in the Andromeda nebula would find the same number. This is why we use it as the basis for attempts at extraterrestrial communication. The whole theory of trying to talk to other civilizations is based on what we are convinced are universal numbers, which anybody would eventually find if they think about mathematics long enough.

So the point I want to make is that there is a platonic world of mathematics which is causally effective, and, therefore, physicists must allow for its existence. It is causally effective in two ways. First we can investigate it as mathematics, which is what I have been talking about. The second is what we briefly touched on last night. There is also some deep relation of the laws of mathematics to the laws of physics, which physicists have speculated about time and again and have not come to any conclusion about. But the fact is that the laws of mathematics are unbelievably effective in describing physical systems.

Hierarchy and the 4 Worlds
[Saturday Morning]

Speaker 8: I am interested in understanding how you came up with four worlds. You seem to have set a rather low threshold for proving the existence of something in one of these worlds, namely that if you can find a word in the dictionary that corresponds to the item. Are these just categories? Is there some very basic thing about these four [worlds] or would somebody else have come up with six or eight or two? So I am proposing two others: the world of sport and the world of music. Where do these fall?

George Ellis: Okay. Firstly, I have not quite got across what I meant by the business of the dictionary. This applies to world two. Under world two I've got three subcategories. Initially, when I did this, I had them separated out. But my colleagues persuaded me that I had far too many worlds and I needed fewer. So I have, under consciousness, three kinds of things: the rational, the intentional, and the socially created. I'm not terribly rigid about that division. It's a provisional division. Now my point about the dictionary is that any concept of a rational kind is in the dictionary, and this, as you say, is slightly arbitrary. Nevertheless, as I tried to make clear in my comment a short while ago, the fact that an idea appears in the dictionary proves that the idea exists. Otherwise it wouldn't be in the dictionary, or in the encyclopedia. This does not mean that there is a corresponding quantity in the real world. For instance, I can have a twin planet to earth in the dictionary. In fact, people have had theories of such a twin earth, but it doesn't actually appear to exist in reality. So the point I was making is that there is a vast array of ideas that definitely exist as ideas. That does not mean that there are corresponding quantities in the real world. These do exist as ideas and they are causally effective as ideas precisely because they have led to a dictionary entry and that dictionary entry is a physical thing. It is marks of ink on paper. So ideas are causally effective in that sense.

There is a different way in which ideas are causally effective, which comes down to the question of plans. The example I used is the plan of a jumbo jet. That is causally effective in the sense that the plan of the jumbo jet then guides people's actions. It guides the way machine tools work and it guides the way that, in the end, a whole mass of metal is produced with a certain conformation. That's a different way in which ideas are causally effective. So ideas are causally effective in two different ways. Firstly, as ideas and secondly, through emotion, as guiding actions.

You suggest the world of sport. That exists firstly in the physical world in the sense that there is a whole lot of paraphernalia, which is the paraphernalia of sport, footballs, jerseys, stadiums, and so on. So the world of sport is made real in physical terms. The fact that sport exists as a category in our minds results in a whole lot of physical activity. But in fact, sport is in that category that I would call social invention because there is a set of rules that were just socially invented. Once they are invented they are causally effective. Yesterday I gave the example of a football match. If you are a statistical physicist and you are looking at a football match you would expect the football to go randomly in all directions, but it doesn't. It is in fact purposely directed toward the goal area. Why? It is directed because of the rules of football. So the laws of sport are invented. They are then written down in books. People talk to each other about them. They exist in people's brains. They exist in these multiple forms, which is why I have said that it is an abstract category, not just a brain-state. It is much more than a brain-state. They [the rules of football] are causally effective because they control, in a very meaningful way, the physical actions, which result in the football, a physical object, moving in certain directions. The world of sport then has a physical expression. But, in a sense, where it really lives is in the world of social construction. The game of chess is a very nice example of the causal effect [of socially constructed rules]. In a chess game, the chess pieces move in rigidly defined ways. Where does that rigid definition come from? It comes from the rules of chess, which are abstract rules.

The world of music and art is a very interesting example as well. This is a much bigger thing than just music. It is the world of art as a whole. There is the question of whether or not art should be given a separate existence. And I am puzzled by that one. I do not know how to handle it. I think you could make a case that it should. The reason I have not written much about this is because I don't know how to do it, and the reason I don't know how to do it is that art is the one area where it is totally apparent that social conditioning is a dominant thing. I do not appreciate Japanese or chamber music, which is a question of social conditioning.

Art exists as a physical form. There is no question about that. And it gets to that physical form because artists have certain concepts in their minds. So it is again the causal efficacy of the mind that results in certain physical things, like sculptures around this campus for instance. The difficult question is related to a topic I will consider later today, and which you have already considered with Nancey Murphy. This is the question of the existence of a moral reality. It seems to me that the underlying question is whether or not there is an aesthetic reality instead of just an aesthetic standard. That puzzles me. In a sense I would like to say there is. But I do not know how to handle it in the view of the absolutely manifest culture dependence of what people think is beautiful.

Speaker 8: The reason I said music and not art is that I think you can at least make a stronger case that there might be an underlying reality in music that is simply discovered rather than invented.

George Ellis: Do we discover certain aspects of music? That's a really interesting question. I have not thought about it. But I believe it is very interesting.

Speaker 9: I remember John Denver talking about finding pieces of music and other artists speaking in the same way of finding something. There seems to be some sense in which you know the notes, or whatever you are seeking, are out there. Finding them is something else again.

George Ellis: Yes. In a certain sense I strongly believe that. And I will talk about this later. But let me say now that there is a kenosis, a giving up, that is central to great art. In undertaking a novel, a play, a piece of sculpture, or a piece of music, you start off with a plan of how it should be and that starts to shape the thing. After a while the thing has its own identity and from then on you either respond to that identity or you do not and that is one of the major differences between great art and trivial art. In a sense that is partly what you are talking about. Once the work has reached a certain stage it has its own identity which you then explore rather than create.

Speaker 10: Is there an immanent or implicit morality in the orders of these worlds?

George Ellis: This is what I will be talking about later. I would say there is a world of morality, which is clearly distinct from these worlds.

Status of the Equations

[Saturday Afternoon]

Speaker 13: Are physical laws prescriptive or descriptive, in other words, one or the other?

George Ellis: I think that's a completely open question. My colleague Bill Stoeger[10] has written about this. He is one of the few people who have, and he thinks they're descriptive. I, along with, I think, most of my scientific colleagues, tend to think of them as prescriptive. However, there is a problem here. We were discussing this at lunch, and the Chair immediately said that Maxwell's equations are prescriptive. And I said "Yes." The problem is that Maxwell's equations are not the correct equations. They [the correct equations] are actually the equations of quantum electrodynamics, because Maxwell's equations are not quantum. They are, therefore, effective equations. And if they are effective, then they are not the fundamental equations. If there are any equations, which are prescriptive rather than descriptive, they should be the fundamental ones, and all the other ones we deal with are effective equations, and not fundamental. Actually we have no idea what the fundamental equations are yet. So the question of whether or not they are prescriptive kind of loses its force. For example the Einstein equations are not the fundamental equations. They're descriptive.

Speaker 15: Could you please define effective equations?

George Ellis: Yes. An effective equation is derived from the fundamental equation and is effective in a certain domain of applicability. For instance, Newton's equations are derived from Einstein's equations and they're extremely effective. Newtonian gravity is very, very effective in the solar system, but [Newton's gravitational equation] is not the fundamental equation. Galilean gravity is derived from Newtonian gravity. For any engineer working on a building, Galilean gravity is all that is required. For that you don't need Newtonian gravity and you do not need Einstein's theory. So the equations of Galilean and Newtonian gravity are effective within certain domains, depending on the circumstances. Many famous theories, such as Fermi's theory of beta decay, are effective and not fundamental theories. In fact if you push this you will find that probably all of the equations we know, including Einstein's equations and the Dirac equation are effective, because we do not yet know the fundamental equations.

For those who are interested in this I would strongly recommend reading the writings Bob Laughlin,[11] who won the Nobel Prize for discovering the theory of the Fractional Quantum Hall Effect. His Nobel Prize lecture is in *Reviews of Modern Physics*.[12] And there's a more recent article by Laughlin and [David] Pines,[13] in the *Proceedings of the National Academy of Science*.[14] There the authors claim that none of the equations we know are the fundamental ones; they are all effective equations.

Aesthetics and the Search for God
Aesthetics and Relationships

Aesthetics and the Search for God
[Sunday]

Speaker 15: A Benedictine abbot from the Cluny Abbey in France, about a thousand years ago, stated that the search for beauty is a way of approaching the Divine. Then St. Bonaventure said that infinite beauty and goodness are two of the attributes of God. Indeed this theme is common to practically all the great medieval theologians.

Can you say something about aesthetics and the relation to God?

George Ellis: The issue of aesthetics I think is very interesting. Perhaps I can put the problem this way. It seems to me, and of course I am an amateur, that a large part of art is ugly, it is not beautiful at all. Diane Arbus is a classic example of someone who takes photographs that are quite deliberately ugly. Now I do not know if that falls within some kind of aesthetical canon or not, but that is art. There is a whole range of art that is intended to shock or to disturb the viewer. I do not know what the relation of that art is to aesthetics. Maybe you have criterion on which you will exclude all of that art as being non-aesthetic. I think I would do that, but then thousands of people would jump on me and say that I do not understand. It would seem then that only a subset art is intended to be beautiful.

That is one problem. Then there is the purely culturally-based aspect. As I discussed earlier, music is an example. I personally cannot relate in any serious sense to Indian or Japanese music, but it is clearly beautiful for Indians and Japanese. This is a problem that I am not sure how to handle. However, there are some books, which have come out recently, dealing with religion and aesthetics. Particularly my colleague John De Gruchy [15] has just published a book on religion and aesthetics in which he makes a strong claim that beauty is a way to understanding God or relating to God. And I agree that the vast body of religious art is proof of that. The huge effort that has gone into religious art, producing cathedrals and so on, shows that people think beauty can bring them close to God. But then there is an opposing group that says that any image is a bad thing because it is ultimately going to mislead you and it will finally become an idol. Therefore images are dangerous. So there is a complicated dynamic there.

Aesthetics and Relationships

[Sunday]

Speaker 7: This is a comment on aesthetics. In the corner of my room where I have my CD player I also have a poster that says, "After silence, that which comes closest to the mind of God is music." Just before playing the Hayden Creation Oratorio, Leonard Bernstein said that God sang the words of creation.

I happen to love baroque music, but I dislike rock and roll and I hate rap music. How does this relate to kenosis? If I would start to try to understand what's behind rap music, and understand what's behind rock and roll music, maybe trying to understand their point of view would bring out kenosis in me. So I think there is a relation between aesthetics and kenosis.

George Ellis: I like what you are saying, in both cases, but I have the same problem [with some music] as I do with some art. I think there is some music that is quite deliberately ugly. So you can, in a kenotic fashion, try to understand what is this about. What is the pain message? But, nevertheless, that music is not for me a route to transcendence, whereas the other music is.

Because it is so subjective I have hesitated in trying to include it in these discussions. I think it is absolutely clear that art provides a way that some people come to experience transcendence. For example, I heard a most beautiful concert in Brno, in the old church where Mendel lived and did his experiments on peas. The Mendel Church in Brno is one of the most beautiful churches I have been to. It was an absolutely transcending experience, listening to singing a bit like the singing we heard today, and the candlelight with these columns going up into the dark in that church. It was absolutely magical.

Speaker 15: My wife, who is an organist, a music director, and a music therapist, was once dealing with a very disturbed, young person. She had to use rap in order to be able to communicate with this young person. So, even though some of the aspects of rap may be displeasing to you, it is a way of getting in touch with and understanding some other people. In this case I think it performed a very useful function.

Kenosis

Discussions Among Religions
Biological Evolution
Fundamentalism
International Conflict
Politics
Psychology, Sociobiology, and Human Communities
Ethics

Discussions Among Religions

[Saturday Afternoon]

Speaker 1: In this morning's lecture you talked about the various viewpoints or positions you would reject, such as dogmatism, and then those that are open including non-dogmatic atheism, non-dogmatic theism, agnosticism, and so forth. And then you pointed out that the ideal is to reach a state of kenosis. As I look at that short list of the good options, I did not see there something that would motivate a person towards a life of kenosis, love, and self-sacrifice. It seems to me that a key motivator has to be present for people to become the kind of folks

118

you would like them to be, because the default option is to look out for number one.

George Ellis: Yes. So what would you see as that motivator?

Speaker 1: What I find appealing is the Christian faith and the example of Jesus Christ is a motivator.

George Ellis: This takes us to the very difficult area of the interfaith dialogue. I agree with you, but the problem is that we live in this globalized world where one can no longer ignore other faiths. There is an enormous amount of faith there [in other religions], and of belief, and of sacrifice. While I agree with you entirely, and that would be my position, and if I did not know about the other faiths that would be the end of the story. But I do [know about other faiths], and that is part of the problem. The other part of the problem is that the term non-dogmatic faith may be misleading. To fully lead a life of kenosis you've got to believe to the hilt in what you're doing. You have got to absolutely believe it, and believe it is worthwhile. Nevertheless, you have to recognize that, from an intellectual viewpoint, this is a leap of faith. It is not certainty. It is not certainty because there is no philosophical or scientific argument that can prove that it is correct. Your personal experience may be such that you cannot deny it. But you have to realize that over there is a Muslim whose personal experience he cannot deny, and over there is a Hindu, and so on. How do you weigh your personal experience against his? All you can say in the end is that you are totally convinced this is the truth, but that you recognize that he has had this personal experience, and for him it's the truth. This is what I mean when I speak of non-dogmatic faith. This is opposed to the situation in which you say, "I know I am right, and therefore you are wrong and your faith is false, and my faith is true."

Biological Evolution

[Saturday Afternoon]

Speaker 16: Is there any evidence of kenosis in biological evolution?

George Ellis: This is an intriguing question. There is evidence of precursors, but true kenosis is the product of understanding and choice. It is not kenosis if it is forced or if it is automatic. The central feature of kenosis is that you voluntarily and freely take certain steps on behalf of the others. And if you have not got self-consciousness then, by definition, you cannot do it. Nevertheless there are precursors. For instance, in ant colonies a large part of the colony sacrifices on behalf of the queen. However, it is not a choice they have made. This is a precursor. It is not the genuine thing. There are of course, throughout the animal kingdom, examples of mothers giving up their lives on behalf of the offspring. Again, that is a precursor. Nevertheless it has some of the qualities of the genuine thing.

I want to say very strongly that the genuine article is seen in people such as Mahatma Gandhi and Martin Luther King. There the action taken is the product of thought and free choice. One of the greatest tragedies occurs when someone sees the power of self-sacrifice and then tries to coerce other people into being self-sacrificial. That was the case, in my reading of the situation, during the Cultural Revolution in China. And this is the reason why such dreadful tragedies happened. Mao Tse Tung saw the power of sacrifice on behalf of others, and then tried to coerce people into sacrificing. This is a total contradiction and led to one of the worst excesses of history.

Speaker 16: Is there any possibility that even Jesus Christ could be subsumed under the evolutionary system?

George Ellis: At one level, in believing that Christ was fully a human being, which is biblical, yes. But, I believe for full religion to make sense there has to be a possibility of divine revelation. Some people are more open to it, others are less. In His [Jesus'] case I would say that His divinity and His being perfectly open to divine revelation would be the essential thing. And that is where something from outside the evolutionary system enters and affects values and understanding in a way that would not be available through the evolutionary system.

Fundamentalism

[Saturday Afternoon]

Speaker 13: Could you comment on what is so attractive about fundamentalism in contrast to kenosis? Is kenosis growing in the world? In the present Middle Eastern situation could we claim that what is being played out is a conflict, or even outright battle, between kenotic and fundamentalist world-views?

George Ellis: Fundamentalism has two attractions, one is intellectual and the other is emotional. Intellectually, fundamentalism results when a partial truth is claimed to be the whole truth. You have fully understood the partial truth and claim that it is the whole truth, which saves you from having to worry about all the other things. There is an enormous number of examples, for instance Freudianism and Darwinism and so on. It is cheap intellectualism.

In emotional terms, fundamentalism relieves you from having to make decisions. You follow the leader of your fundamental faith, who tells you what to do. You do not have to make any decisions. Following the leader is a terribly comfortable and easy thing to do. Adolf Hitler says this, that, and the other, and you go out and you do it. You give up your own integrity and have all of your problems solved. You no longer have to think; you just follow. That is easy.

Is kenosis growing in the world or not? That is a very difficult question. I'm hoping that it is. My two paradigms for its practical application are Martin Luther King and Mahatma Gandhi. There's a fabulous book about Martin Luther King entitled *Martin Luther King, Jr.: The Making of a Mind*[16] that describes how King, after receiving a doctorate in theology, thought about this [non-violence] for fifteen years before starting to practice these ideas politically. He did not simply gather the brothers together and head off. Gandhi did exactly the same kind of thing. It is very difficult and very costly. I think what we are lacking at the moment are figureheads to drive this. For a time Desmond Tutu and Nelson Mandela were paradigms of kenosis. But since they have both retired, I do not see any major public figure on the world-stage promoting kenosis in the way that they were.

Mother Teresa has inspired hundreds of thousands of people to do much the same thing as she did. Such works are tremendous, and I am not downgrading what they are saying or doing. But it does not have the same implications as [the works of] people like Mahatma Gandhi and Martin Luther King who bring kenosis into the political arena and begin influencing the lives of nations.

The big international movement for kenosis, which is partly and falteringly underway, is the United Nations. This is an embodiment of the idea that nations should give up their sovereignty to an international body, which is the basis of kenosis. It has happened to some degree. There is also a world court, which has jurisdiction over certain things. It is a faltering movement precisely because the United Nations has never really become what it could have been. But it is the potential body through which kenosis could become practical at the international level.

Someone said to me today, and I agree with him, that we are facing a crisis. Let me take just a minute to put this in its historical context. How long have we had consciousness? We have probably had real consciousness for something like fifty thousand years. Each individual and each group has a particular conscious understanding, and you are threatened when you encounter an individual or group with a different understanding. Your immediate response is to get rid of them. That appears to be the only way to solve the problem, and that is the way we solved it for thousands of years. But in the past couple of hundred years we have said, "Look, you do not have to slaughter people with an opposite understanding; you can tolerate them." The next step is to realize that we can actually learn from them. This is the change that has been taking place through democracy and internationalism. This change has been enormously successful in many ways. Nevertheless, there is what I call an ethical transition that has to take place.

The power to destroy humanity through the development of technology is increasing through biological weapons as well as nuclear weapons. If you ask yourself whether humanity is going to survive for another thousand years, or five thousand, or ten thousand, you realize that the chances are pretty slim. The reason is that there is a good chance that someone, who is a fundamentalist of some religion, will get possession of these weapons of mass destruction and decide that the time has come to end it. Oklahoma City is an example of Christian fundamentalism. September 11 is an example of Islamic fundamentalism. We are only going to stop that if we have an international, global ethical transition that moves us from a coercive to a kenotic form [of encounter]. And that is why it is incredibly important that these international bodies, such as the UN, try to work for this kind of transition. I am quite optimistic in that I think there are a growing number of bodies trying to make this transition happen. However, it is a race against time. It is a race to see whether the ethical attempts or the technological attempts will win.

Speaker 17: My question goes back to your comments on fundamentalism, and it also has to do with the political situation. You said that it is very important to be fully committed to what you believe. But aren't there many, many millions of people who do not have the time or the education or the knowledge to really make such a commitment? Many people do not know what they are really doing when it comes to faith. So they just jump in, and do the best they can. They really want to be committed, and this is part of the problem with fundamentalism. There is a need to be committed, but sometimes people do not have the knowledge to do it well.

George Ellis: I would agree with that, but I would not equate that with poverty, or simplicity. There is this tremendous need for commitment and an understanding, but it seems to me that part of the message of Jesus was that it isn't necessarily the intelligent or the rich who are the people who will have the right commitment to the right cause. He sought out the people who were not of that kind. So I would agree with you, excepting that you seemed to be suggesting that there were people who were too poor or who did not have the time. I do not think that is relevant. I think the poorest person, in the worst conditions, always has opportunities to react in a kenotic way. I think it is a question of spiritual understanding, which is available to all.

Speaker 15: I just have a very brief comment regarding what you said about the end of World War II. I was there. And I know for a fact that, had it not been for the Marshall Plan, Europe would have been a wrecked continent. And I think it is the same thing that we are going to have to do both in Afghanistan and in Palestine, after we have either destroyed them or allowed them to be destroyed. We should now come back and really use this kenotic opportunity.

George Ellis: There are the leaders and the followers, and, as I have said, there is a psychotic element in all populations. Somehow you have to deal with that in practical, political terms. Even if you would like to be kenotic, you might not be able to. Regardless of the specific leadership, there is always the vast body of the population. What you can do is offer the majority some vision of the future, some hope, some way out, in which you are not penalizing them for what they have done, even if they have been associated with horrific things. And that is where the kenotic response would come through.

International Conflict

[Saturday Afternoon]

Speaker 3: I wonder if there could be a kenotic response to 9-11. You said today that true security was more possible through the process of kenosis than through a forceful control. Did you have any personal reflections on this in mid-September [2001]? Do you think something like the spirit that motivated the South African Truth and Reconciliation Commission could pervade the situation between the leaders of the US and other Western countries and leaders in the Islamic world, or between Palestine and Israel?

George Ellis: I am a strong advocate of kenosis. However, people like John Polkinghorne, with whom I have talked, and even Desmond Tutu have said that the key issue in kenosis is the readiness to act in a sacrificial way, but that does not necessarily mean you always would act in a sacrificial way. I think that is correct and very important. The problem here is that in any large population there are always psychotic individuals who are temporarily or permanently beyond the reach of reason, and even of kenotic action. And so, regrettably, there have to be some mechanisms that can try to cope with this situation.

Nevertheless, the central concept in Christianity, which is explicitly expressed by Quakers, is that every person has the light of Christ within, and is a person who is redeemable. How do you redeem them? You redeem them by approaching them in a way that somehow catches them off guard. You do not respond to them the way they want. It is moral jujitsu if you like.

What the perpetrators of September 11 wanted was a military response. They would have been totally thrown by a non-military response. That is, of course, futile speculation because they got the military response. But the whole point about the kenotic response is that the other sees you as the enemy and wants you to see him as the enemy. When you do not see him as the enemy, but as a redeemable human being, he finds the situation very difficult to handle. But, it is very, very difficult to put that kind of thing into practice. I have already said that it was immensely costly for Mahatma Gandhi and Martin Luther King, and it took an immense amount of time, preparation and effort. Nevertheless they showed that in certain circumstances it does work.

In the case of September 11, given the situation you are in now, I would say that the kenotic response would come in rebuilding the Afghan nation. I think the Americans, through their actions, have created a commitment to the Afghan people. And the question is whether they will fulfill that commitment or not.

There is an incredible difference between what happened at the end of the First World War, and the end of the Second World War. At the end of the First World War there was a non-kenotic response—the Treaty of Versailles, which put in place conditions that guaranteed that the Second World War would take place. That lesson was learned, and at the end of the Second World War, despite everything the German people had done, only some of them were put on trial, and the German people as a whole were not treated as criminals. On the contrary, they were treated in a kenotic way. The United States gave huge amounts of aid to Germany and to Japan, through the Marshall Plan, in a way that enabled them to rebuild. I think that was a kenotic action, which has paid off because it put in place a totally different situation from the previous one.

Speaker 3: I understand the sort of consciousness you see emerging here, especially since World War II. But we're not quite there yet. It seems that Kenosis has two aspects to it. Firstly, not grasping at sovereignty, and secondly, being subject to death. No nation would subject itself to death. In submitting to the world court or to various UN treaties each nation reserves the right to defend itself. This is a sort of third way, but this third way is still far short of the way of Jesus.

George Ellis: I agree.

Politics

[Saturday Afternoon]

Speaker 9: It seems to me that kenosis is an unattainable goal in practical politics. I understand that in South Africa there is a Quaker woman who is secretary of war, is that true? I would like to know how that is possible.

George Ellis: The deputy minister of defense is a black, Quaker woman who is a member of our Cape Town meeting. The basic answer is that Quakers are very tolerant people.

There has been debate in the Quaker movement over the years. At one point it was felt untypical that Quakers held any position of power whatever, but many Quakers have taken positions of power in civil society. The position is somewhat paradoxical. If one enters political activity then one becomes engaged in the art of the possible. So while this woman is deputy minister of defense she is in a position to make some kind of difference that she would not be able to make otherwise. This is obviously a very debatable position. The broader question is, "Should Quakers take up, as others do, such positions of political power?" What is the position of Mennonites on this issue?

Speaker 8: It is roughly the same. A similar debate is going on in the Mennonite Church. There are now Mennonites in government, which was uncommon a generation ago.

George Ellis: Well, you see, there are problems and opportunities either way. One position is to claim that we are going to keep it pure and we shall not take any part in power. And so the people in power say, "Well that is fine, but that means that your policies are impractical and you refuse to get into a position of power because they are impractical."

The Great Quaker Experiment of course was Pennsylvania, William Penn and all of that. That worked for a couple of hundred years or so, and many people would say it was very successful. But as soon as you engage in practical politics things will start going wrong. There are going to be conflicts and so on.

I think the basic viewpoint would be that true kenosis is, in the end, probably an almost unattainable goal. To really undertake this you have got to spend your entire life on it, like Mahatma Gandhi and Martin Luther King. But to the extent that one manages to introduce a kenotic element into life things are going to be made better. We mentioned a few examples yesterday. The way that the Allies handled the ending of the Second World War was far more kenotic than the way they handled the end of the First World War, and that made a huge practical difference to the world in the past fifty years.

Psychology, Sociobiology, and Human Communities

[Sunday]

Speaker 18: If kenosis is transformative of a person's relationships and situations, can science explain how kenosis works? In general, what aspect of, or what branch of science can explain kenosis or the influence of kenotic events?

George Ellis: Well, it depends on what science you are talking about. I cannot see chemistry or physics having anything to say about it. But it is very relevant to psychology and to an understanding of history. This is where the Templeton Foundation has been doing interesting work. For example, they have recently been funding a program on forgiveness research. This has resulted in a series of publications that are available through the Templeton press. Forgiveness is closely related to kenosis. The Templeton Foundation has funded some serious psychological studies dealing with the effect of forgiveness on health. That is very interesting. But what that does not consider is the effect of forgiveness on public life.

As an example of the effect of kenosis on history, there is South African Truth and Reconciliation Commission, for which forgiveness was a central part. There is also the Restorative Justice Movement.[17] This is a small, but growing movement, based on forgiveness. It is a practical kenotic movement.

Speaker 18: You previously dismissed socio-biology pretty easily, and I may too. But there is the interest among socio-biologists in reciprocal altruism. It would seem that there is no better example of kenosis than reciprocal altruism. There is also a lot of primate research by Frans De Waal and others.

George Ellis: That is clearly an interesting and important issue. It has a subset related to Game Theory, and it is partly based in evolution.
Frans de Waal's work is particularly relevant. But in my opinion, that research can and has been successful only to the degree it has explained what I would call shallow ethics. In other words, we are going to fight for our own family and our own kin. It does not begin to explain how you can exercise forgiveness towards your enemies. That is the Christian approach. The Games Theory connection might potentially be able to do so, but has not. We recently had a meeting in Princeton about this. There we tried to interest others in the Games Theory models that would consider kenosis, but there was little interest. Still, that is a possibility.

Speaker 18: Most of your examples about kenosis have dealt with particular historic leader figures and historical situations. And you have said that people of faith all have a kenotic element in their ethics. And then you also described the progress in human experience, indicating that human relations were not as bad as they were a hundred or a thousand years ago. But if one goes back farther to pre-history, to primal, foraging kinds of societies, one finds that those were embodiments of kenotic life.

George Ellis: That is a very interesting point. I would like to see some evidence of that. It could well be true that the advent of large-scale societies has undermined a possible kenotic aspect of primal society. I would be slightly cautious with this, however. One society that is often held up as an ideal is that of the Bushman. In that society the elderly, who cannot keep up during migration, are simply left behind. There is something related to this that I find interesting. There is a subliterature on communities dealing with how communities function, the problems of communities and the way to form communities. I think that is very relevant.

   I want to come back very briefly to the issue of forgiveness, which is closely related to kenosis. There are courses in Life-Training, run by the Kairos[18] foundation. This is one of the many organizations giving courses on how to improve your life. This particular one I happen to like, and I have taken part in it. One section is on resentment, and it is fascinating. People in the course write down resentments they have held in their lives, against brothers, sisters, mothers-in-law, children, parents, and so on. And then they are asked to write down how many years they have held each resentment and to add up the years. In the last course I went to, there were thirty-five people, and the added result cam out to be twenty-eight hundred years of resentment. It is fascinating. Why do people hold on to resentments? What is it that motivates you to hang on to that resentment against your mother for what happened thirty years ago? There are payoffs to resentment. You feel morally superior, among other things. But then the sessions consider the costs of resentment. The costs of resentment include health, money, lost opportunities and so on. Finally the course presents practical ways of dealing with resentment. This is a process of kenosis. It is giving up, because the definition of resentment is long-term ill will held against some other person or body. As long as you hold onto it you are ruining your life more than anybody else's life. And when you give it up, you improve your life more than anybody else's life.

God's Action

Scholars Involved

[Saturday Afternoon]

Speaker 14: Could you give a little survey of the disciplinary landscape of some of the other leading thinkers in the field, such as Arthur Peacocke, John Polkinghorne, Ian Barbour, and others. And then if you could comment on some of the differences, or give us your views on where other scholars are so we understand the whole context here.

George Ellis: I must be careful here. I know a particular set of scholars, but I cannot claim to know all of them. One of the interesting things that has happened through the Science and the Spiritual Quest project, is that there has been an attempt to start forming a link among scholars in Asia, Latin America, and Europe, France, Spain, Germany and so on. Many of these people have been working in isolation, and have not been part of the debate in which I have been engaged. So I think it is very important to realize there is a worldwide discussion which is gradually getting connected.

The people I have been particularly connected with are those who are part of the Vatican/CTNS team. They have been very carefully selected, so they are a good team. Barbour is a process theologian, and together with Nancey [Murphy] I like that [process theology] to some degree. But in the end I find some of it very uncomfortable. I am a little wary of process philosophy and theology, even though it is broadly, I think, going in the right direction.

I have a great deal of sympathy with Peacocke[19] for two reasons. He is one of the people who have talked very clearly about top-down action. As you have gathered from the way I talk, I think this is absolutely crucial, and absolutely central to the whole thing. Without top-down action, reductionism wins; with top-down action, reductionism does not win. I think it is that simple. Also Peacocke very much believes in a kenotic form of action. So I like that very much as well. Nevertheless, in terms of divine action Peacocke talks about, and believes in, some kind of generalized top-down action without specifying a mechanism that lets it happen. The issue here is that the central place where top-down action gets into the physical world is through the human mind and the nervous system in the human body, which is highly directed. It is highly directed so that through some switching mechanism, which we do not understand, you have a thought that you are going to move a particular muscle and that muscle moves. This is the result of a physical link from the brain down to the muscle. But I cannot see what causal mechanism there could be in the universe that would allow Peacocke's generalized concept of top-down action to lead to specific reactions in the human brain.

Polkinghorne is, to some degree, constrained from being very adventurous in this field. In this debate on divine action, he has been pushing the idea that chaos theory is the key. He talks a lot about how the fact that chaos theory has removed strict predictability from physics. This, in his opinion, opens up a possibility, which could be utilized in order for God to act in the world without in any way violating the laws of physics. But I do not see any causal mechanism here by which specific information could be conveyed.

A person whose writing I find very nice is Tom Tracy.[20] He's a philosopher, and has written in the Vatican/CTNS series. Any of you who are philosophers will find his writing very beautiful and precise. He goes along with Nancey [Murphy], whom you have heard talk, and with me in pushing the quantum uncertainty option. The quantum uncertainty option says that, from the viewpoint of physicists, there is this total uncertainty about what happens at the micro-level. But the fact that human beings are unable to specify this does not mean that God cannot specify. So one must be very precise here. Some people say, "But all this means is that God is acting in a totally unpredictable way." My answer to that is to say, "No, that is a misunderstanding." If one follows the quantum route one sees that for human beings it's uncertain, but for God it is not. And the physicist's dogma that quantum uncertainty is ontological not epistemological is simply wrong. On the contrary, God is a hidden variable in terms of Physics. The physical theorems then say that it [the hidden variable] must then be non-local. And we say that God acts non-locally, and that is fine. And so Tom Tracy, Nancey [Murphy], and many others, as well as I, push this view. I am, however, not claiming a complete representation of the group.

Bill Stoeger is a very thoughtful scientist/theologian, who writes in sentences that stretch through paragraphs, but he is always worth reading because he is very thoughtful about all of this. There is also a group of scientists who are very interested in this debate such as Paul Davies and John Barrow. They are both superb scientific communicators, and they both have an immense grasp of the nature of science, and its broader philosophical implications, and anything that either of them writes is always worth reading.

God's Action, the Laws of Physics and Kenosis
[Saturday Morning]

Speaker 6: God is ultimately at the top of the causal hierarchy. However, God is bound by or constrained by a bottom-up causality that the laws of physics give. This evidently indicates a bottom-up causality that constrains God's action in the world so that God is not free in the world to do whatever God wants.

Even though God chose the laws there is still the question of the nature of God. God is evidently choosing the law that places a limit on our understanding of the omnipotence of God. Is it a qualified omnipotence? Is this just sort of a subjective omnipotence? And one can say the same of the laws of ethics. The rules of ethics are chosen to be whatever God wanted. But once they are chosen then God is bound to abide by them. God can always change the laws, but then we would know something was up.

George Ellis: Let us start at the bottom. I believe God has voluntarily chosen to put the specific set of laws of physics in place. And having made that decision God chooses to abide by it (almost always). If one takes that position it is logically conceivable that God could decide, for some temporary purposes, to suspend those laws or put other laws in place. Now that is a very dangerous kind of thing for a whole host of reasons, which are mainly theological.

There is, of course, a physical problem as well. The physical problem is that you then have a region of space where the laws of physics are different. There is then a boundary between regions of space in which the laws of physics are different. This is physically a bit of a problem. But the real problem is a theological one.

As soon as God starts suspending the laws for one reason then the question is why didn't he do it for some other reason? Why didn't he stop my toothache? Why did he allow Auschwitz to take place? As soon as you claim that God is suspending the laws of physics you end up on the slippery slope, which has major theological problems apart from its repugnance to physicists.

So let's go the physics route. God is choosing to keep them [the laws]. I have not yet made my position clear on this, so let me do so. The way I see God's action taking place in the world at the present time is that this quantum uncertainty is basically used for one purpose, which is to convey informational pre-images (or something) into the human brain. This means that spiritual life has a reality to it. There is a vast body of literature about spiritual life and I am assuming here that some of that is not delusion. So you need a channel into the human brain, and this [through quantum indeterminacy] is the way I see this happening. The question of energy conservation has been raised in this. Does this interaction involve violation of any kind of conservation? I do not want to go into detail on this. But the way I see the situation is that in the neurons there are excited atomic states that decay and when they decay they send off a signal which now travels down [the axon] and conveys various bits of information. Of course quantum theory is unable to tell you when an excited state will decay. There is absolutely no prediction that atomic physics can make there. And so I would see the possibility of conveying information as being through some hidden variable. The decision is made to convey the information by controlling when excited states decay. That would be something that is very conceivable.

Now the question of quantum statistics arises. Here there are problems. Firstly, in any living system you have not got the kind of quasi equilibrium states to which normal statistics applies. The biological system is nowhere near equilibrium. Secondly there isn't actually any proof that ordinary statistical physics works inside the human brain and it may or may not actually apply in that kind of far from equilibrium situation. The statistics you would want for radioactive decay is that which results in a half-life for a whole mass of objects. But in the brain you do not have an assemblage of atoms which are all decaying. There are individual ones, and so the question is, does quantum statistics apply to individual brain states in the complex structure? Maybe it does and maybe it does not. It is something we could debate.

Speaker 6: Then you still maintain God's sovereignty?

George Ellis: Yes. And this is the idea of kenosis to which I have referred and to which I am sure Nancey [Murphy] referred as well. God's decision is to respect the integrity of the creation that he has made and to respect the kind of qualities of action, which he has created in those objects. God's decision is not to supervene in a forceful way, in a coercive way, to change their nature from what has been given as their intrinsic nature.

Speaker 7: It seems to me that we have to include the idea of mystery in all of this discussion about God. Trying to determine how God acts is what Einstein tried to do in his discussions with Bohr when he [Einstein] was disagreeing with the uncertainty principle [indeterminacy principle]. Einstein said "God does not play dice." And Bohr replied, "Don't tell God what to do!" Mystery is a part of the question that we always have to consider.

John Haught of Georgetown University has pointed out that God respects the creation God made. This is the kenosis that you just mentioned. Therefore, what happens in evolution, through the laws that God originally made, is just what happens. What God does is to bring good out of some possible evil. There is much good that came out of what happened in 9/11.[21] God may not play dice, but we must not tell God what to do.

George Ellis: I agree with you. There is mystery but I take it you are not saying we shouldn't engage in theology. We have to do our best and we understand it is going to be incomplete and partial. But I agree with John Haught. God does respect the nature of creation.

God and Higher Dimensions
[Saturday Morning]

Speaker 1: We said earlier that God creates the laws of the universe and then obeys them. I want to focus on the word "then." We as human beings have a very severe limitation in our way of thinking. We are time-sequential. We nod assent to the concept of God's ability to be at all times at once, but hardly ever do we really grasp this. The creation by God, in the framework that includes both space and time, is comprenhesive and does not imply that God must behave sequentially. The idea that step one is to create laws and step two is to obey them is a time-dependent statement. We cannot imply God's obliged behavior when those obligations, in fact, are created by our own limited way of thinking about time.

George Ellis: Perhaps what I would add to that is that there is a resource from theoretical physics which one may or may not want to use to model the nature of God's transcendence. Transcendence, as I would understand it, is, in its nature, quite different from the things that are transcended. A transcendent world would be different from all four of the worlds I have talked about. Otherwise it would not be transcendent. A resource from theoretical physics is the idea of the imbedding of a space in a higher dimensional space. This is now one of the major themes in a number of areas of theoretical physics. Is our four dimensional world embedded in a five dimensional one, which is a current theory of cosmology being touted by various people, or in an eleven-dimensional one, as string theory says? In this way one can easily conceive of the existence of God in a higher dimensional space. The points you make are, in this context, then completely obvious. And God, in that higher dimensional space, is not constrained by the causal laws of the lower dimensional space. This provides a kind of setting within which one can talk about that.

Speaker 1: Throughout the weekend, we have often considered that God is a higher dimension. And there are these other worlds, with dimension above that of the physical world, in which, in some way, the relationship with God occurs. And yet again and again, there's this retreat back to the laws of physics and quantum uncertainty. But the laws of physics are in a four-dimensional space. If God is out there in an infinite dimensional space, and if we have these other worlds that put us in higher dimensional spaces, why do we try to shoehorn or otherwise squeeze this interaction with God into the world of the four dimensions of quantum mechanics?

George Ellis: Because we want the four-dimensional world to be reliable. So the arguments I have made refer to that four-dimensional world in which we have our existence, and within which we carry out our moral action. This is true regardless of what may be going on in higher dimensions.

Speaker 1: But we have our existence made out of atoms. And you have, right from Friday night, said that we have all these other worlds too that are part of our existence.

George Ellis: If you are going to ask me in what dimensions do those other worlds exist, I have absolutely no answer. I do not know. The physicist has no idea how the laws of physics are imposed on matter. They know they are, but they do not know how. It comes back to this fascinating thing. Just by naming something, we think we understand it. We call this thing the law of gravity, and now we understand it. But that doesn't get us any nearer to understanding how the moon over there pulls on us over here. We say there's a force of gravity, so we give it a name, and now we understand it. But we are no nearer fundamental understanding than before we gave it that name.

God's Interaction and Prayer

[Sunday]

Speaker 13: Your earlier comments indicated that you have considered models of how God might direct or even manipulate events by acting within the bounds of quantum indeterminacy. Have you reflected at all on the nature of intercessory prayer in this or a similar context? The question is whether humans have that same capability of impacting a specific event. If that were the case, we would end up as part of the mind of God.

George Ellis: Intercessory prayer is a very difficult one. One of the positions, to which I would certainly subscribe, is that intercessory prayer has a very good effect on the persons engaged in the prayer. Their prayer may change their understanding and their actions in a very positive way. If we're talking about praying for rain, I think you can probably count me out. That does not mean that if I really get desperate I might not go out and pray for rain.

Speaker 21: There are the results of intercessory prayer, as in the Charles Grandison Finney Revivals.[22] In these revivals people were prayed for in their presence as a way of impacting them.

George Ellis: Someone has recently enlightened me on Lourdes and the Catholic Church in Lourdes. There is a commission that investigates claims of miracles at Lourdes with the highest technical standards.[23] I think they have pronounced about six or seven cures during the whole time that people have been to Lourdes having put them through the most rigorous testing.

Speaker 9: There is one very remarkable cure that's detailed by Alexis Carrel.[24] He took a patient of his to Lourdes and actually saw the swelling in this woman's [the patient's] stomach going down. He describes it in a book that probably goes back to the early 1900s or something like that. And he tested her both before and afterwards.

George Ellis: The real problems in such cases are actually theological and not physical. If cures are possible then why does God allow thousands and millions of people to die without a cure?

Speaker 22: Is prayer a form of direct interaction with the divine, or is it just an illusion?

George Ellis: The central faith of the Quaker meeting is that in the silence one encounters God, and that [encounter] is not an illusion. There is a whole list of versions of prayers such as praise and thanksgiving. There are surely people here who are much better able to talk to you about this than I am because we do not have formal prayers like other churches do. We believe strongly in listening to God in silence and it is up to the individual if they want to engage in intercessory prayer, or praise, or thanksgiving. But if religious life makes sense, and if religious practice makes sense, then there has to be some meaning to prayer. I have pointed out that from the viewpoint of a physicist, if one wants to, one can make a channel for that to happen through quantum uncertainty. Now you may or may not want to pursue that. But it is possible.

God's Interaction and Free Will
[Sunday]

Speaker 4: How would you define the notion of free will? Then suppose God has an intention to influence me in regard to evil acts, and so he tweaks some quantum indeterminacy in relation to that evil and influences me. Wouldn't that interfere with my free will?

George Ellis: I do not have a definition of free will. It is one of those things that we recognize and cannot define. Basically the existence of free will implies that we have the ability to choose between alternative futures. We have a real ability to weigh the alternatives and to make a responsible decision about them. And if I do one thing rather than the other, I can be held accountable for it. I am very careful about the way in which I phrase this.

I believe that God is kenotic and that God's interaction with me is of a kenotic nature. That means that any images or intimations of transcendence available to me are persuasive and not coercive. Denis Edwards[25] has written about this. The whole point about it is that if God has the powers we attribute to God, God could easily force us.

I am suggesting that the kenotic interaction God has with us is the sort of thing that occurs in the Quaker meeting or in your prayer meetings. There you consciously open yourself to divine understanding and certain intimations of what would be the right thing. The light of God in you makes certain visions or ideas available, and you then have the choice of accepting them or not. It seems unfair, however, that God makes such visions available to some people alone. Why only Saul? Why not everybody? And, in a sense, it is unfair. Some people have this strong feeling of the presence of God, and others do not, and that is unfair to those who do not. I cannot comment on that, except to say that I believe that those who are ready for such messages may have them, and those who are not ready may not.

Notes

Preface

[1] Nancey Murphy and George F. R. Ellis, *On the Moral Nature of the Universe*
[2] See *Quantum Mechanics: Scientific Perspectives on Divine Action*.

Lecture 2

[1] Jacques L. Monod
[2] Amy Biehl was killed by black youth while she was working in a South African township for their liberation. Her family have reconciled with the killers and set up a foundation to help them.

Lecture 3

[1] Peter Atkins
[2] Daniel C. Dennett
[3] Richard Dawkins
[4] Carl Sagan
[5] Jacques Lucien Monod
[6] William A. Dembski
[7] Karl R. Popper
[8] Eccles, John

Teaching: Sunday Worship

[1] Claus Westermann, *Genesis 1—11, a Commentary*, trans. John J. Scullion S.J. (Minneapolis: Augsburg Publishing House, 1984) : 1-73. This is indispensible reading for an understanding of the genealogy in Genesis. It needs updating by R.R. Wilson, *Sociological Approaches to the Old Testament*, Philadelphia., 1984.

[2] Alex Haley, *Roots* (Garden City, New York: Doubleday & Company Inc., 1976).

[3] *ANET*: 265.

[4] Cf. ANET:4ff, 60ff, 501ff.

[5] Similarly to this Babylonian creation epic, *The Theology of Memphis* states that Upper and Lower Egypt are united by kingship, the political power principle (ANET:6a).

[6] *NYT*, sec. 4, 7/19/01, pp. 1, 14.

[7] The Priestly writer's demything or "de-pantheizing" is most evident in God's creating and blessing the great "sea monsters" (*tanninim*, 1:21, 22), which elsewhere is translated *dragons* (Isa. 27:1; 51:9, KJV). In Near East mythology they are chaotic creatures which oppose the gods of order. Even Psalm 74:13 regards these monsters more mythologically, who in the Exodus story oppose God at the sea.

[8] The *NYT* writes, "In a startling about-face, the National Association of Biology teachers, which had long stood firm against religious fundamentalists who insisted that creationism be taught in public schools, recently excised two key words from its platform on teaching evolution."

" 'The diversity of life on earth,' the group's platform used to read, 'is the outcome of evolution: an unsupervised, impersonal, unpredictable, and natural process.' Now the crucial words 'unsupervised' and 'impersonal' have been dropped. The revision is clearly designed to allow for the possibility that a Master Hand was at the helm" (*NYT*, Dec. 21, 1997, Section 4, 1). Before this revision, the National Association was as guilty as the Creationists of confusing their "religion" (not unlike the pantheism of ancient Near East myths) with their science.

[9] Cf. Ian G. Barbour, *Religion and Science, Historical and Contemporary Issues*, 1971. For a history of science in relation to the Bible's teaching on creation, see Christopher Kaiser, *Creation and the History of Science* (London: Marshall Pickering; Grand Rapids: William B. Eerdmans Publishing Co., 1991).

[10] Cf. Paul, Romans 8:22-23.

Discussions

[1] Astronomer Royal, Professor Sir Martin Rees, *Before the Beginning: Our Universe and Others*.

[2] David Chalmers, Dept. of Philosophy, University of Arizona.

[3] *The Balance Within*: The Science Connecting Health and Emotions by Esther M. Sternberg M.D.

[4] Robert John Russell

[5] CTNS: Center for Theology and the Natural Sciences.

[6] The bases contained in the DNA molecule: (C) cytosine, (G) guanine, (A) adenine, and (T) thymine

[7] Gerald Edelman, *Neural Darwinism: The Theory of Neuronal Group Selection*.

[8] Antonio R. Damasio, *Descartes' Error: Emotion, Reason, and the Human Brain*.

[9] William R. Stoeger, S.J.

[10] William R. Stoeger, S.J.

[11] Robert B. Laughlin

[12] R.B. Laughlin, 1999, Nobel Lecture: Fractional Quantization, *Reviews of Modern Physics*, vol. 71, No. 4, 863-874.

[13] David Pines

[14] R.B. Laughlin and David Pines, 2000, The Theory of Everything, *Proceedings of the National Academy of Science* (PNAS), vol. 97, no. 1, 28-31.

[15] John W. De Gruchy, *Christianity, Art and Transformation : Theological Aesthetics in the Struggle for Justice*.

[16] John J. Ansbro, *Martin Luther King, Jr.: The Making of a Mind*

[17] Restorative justice is a systematic response to crime that emphasizes healing the wounds of victims, offenders and communities caused or revealed by the criminal behavior. http://www.restorativejustice.org/

[18] http://www.kairosfoundation.org.

[19] Arthur Peacocke

[20] Thomas F. Tracy

[21] 9/11 refers to the terrorist attack in New York on September 11, 2001.

[22] Charles Grandison Finney (1830s) was the foremost American revivalist between George Whitefield (1700s) and Dwight Lyman Moody (late 1800s).

[23] When the file is sent to the Bishop of the place where the cured person lives, the case is already recognized as extraordinary by science and medically inexplicable. It remains for the Church, through the intermediary of the Bishop, to make an announcement on the miraculous character of the cure. To do this, the Bishop gathers together a Diocesan Canonical Commission made up of priests, canonists, and theologians. The rules that guide the procedures of this Commission are those defined in 1734 by the future Pope Benedict XIV in his treatise: Concerning the Beatification and Canonisation of Servants of God (Book IV, Part I, Chapter VIII nø2). Source: http://www.lourdes-france.org/gb/gbsb0027.htm

[24] Alexis Carrel, (1873-1944).

[25] Denis Edwards, *Human Experience of God*

Index

About Pandora Press

Pandora Press is a small, independently owned press dedicated to making available modestly priced books that deal with Anabaptist, Mennonite, and Believers Church topics, both historical and theological. We welcome comments from our readers.

Visit our full-service online Bookstore:
www.pandorapress.com

Karl Koop. *Anabaptist-Mennonite Confessions of Faith: the Development of a Tradition.* (forthcoming 2003)
  Softcover. ISBN 1-894710-32-0

Mary A. Schiedel. *Pioneers in Ministry: Women Pastors in Ontario Mennonite Churches, 1973-2003.* (2003)
  Softcover, 204 pp. ISBN 1-894710-35-5

Harry Loewen, ed. *Shepherds, Servants and Prophets.* (2003)
  Softcover, 446 pp. ISBN 1-894710-31-2

Robert A. Riall, trans., Galen A. Peters, ed. *The Earliest Hymns of the Ausbund: Some Beautiful Christian Songs Composed and Sung in the Prison at Passau, Published in 1564.* (2003)
  Softcover, 473 pp., bibliography, index. ISBN 1-894710-34-7

John A. Harder. *From Kleefeld With Love.* (2003)
  Softcover, 198 pp. ISBN 1-894710-28-2

John F. Peters. *The Plain People: A Glimpse at Life Among the Old Order Mennonites of Ontario.* (2003)
  Softcover, 54 pp. ISBN 1-894710-26-6

Robert S. Kreider. *My Early Years: An Autobiography.* (2002)
  Softcover, 600 pp., index. ISBN 1-894710-23-1

Helen Martens. *Hutterite Songs.* (2002)
  Softcover, xxii, 328 pp. ISBN 1-894710-24-X

C. Arnold Snyder and Galen A. Peters, eds. *Reading the Anabaptist Bible: Reflections for Every Day of the Year.* Introduction by Arthur Paul Boers. (2002)
  Softcover, 415 pp. ISBN 1-894710-25-8

C. Arnold Snyder, ed. *Commoners and Community. Essays in Honour of Werner O. Packull.* (2002)
  Softcover, 324 pp. ISBN 1-894710-27-4

James O. Lehman. *Mennonite Tent Revivals: Howard Hammer and Myron Augsburger, 1952-1962.* (2002)
  Softcover, xxiv, 318 pp., index. ISBN 1-894710-22-3

Lawrence Klippenstein and Jacob Dick. *Mennonite Alternative Service in Russia.* (2002)
  Softcover, viii, 163 pp. ISBN 1-894710-21-5

Nancey Murphy. *Religion and Science.* (2002)
  Softcover, 126 pp. ISBN 1-894710-20-7

Biblical Concordance of the Swiss Brethren, 1540. Trans. by Gilbert Fast and Galen Peters; introduction by Joe Springer; C. Arnold Snyder, ed. (2001)
  Softcover, lv, 227 pp., index. ISBN 1-894710-16-9

Orland Gingerich. *The Amish of Canada.* (2001)
  Softcover, 244 pp., index. ISBN 1-894710-19-3

M. Darrol Bryant. *Religion in a New Key.* (2001)
  Softcover, 136 pp., bibliography. ISBN 1-894710-18-5

Sources of South German/Austrian Anabaptism. Trans. by Walter Klaassen, Frank Friesen, Werner O. Packull; C. Arnold Snyder, ed. (2001)
  Softcover, 430 pp., indices. ISBN 1-894710-15-0

Pedro A. Sandín Fremaint y Pablo A. Jimémez. *Palabras Duras: Homilías.* (2001)
  Softcover, 121 pp. ISBN 1-894710-17-7

James C. Juhnke and Carol M. Hunter. *The Missing Peace: The Search for Nonviolent Alternatives in United States History.* (2001)
  Softcover, 321 pp., index. ISBN 1-894710-13-4

Ruth Elizabeth Mooney. *Manual Para Crear Materiales de Educación Cristiana.* (2001)
  Softcover, 206 pp. ISBN 1-894710-12-6

Esther and Malcolm Wenger, poetry by Ann Wenger. *Healing the Wounds.* (2001)
  Softcover, 210 pp. ISBN 1-894710-09-6

Pedro A. Sandín Fremaint. *Cuentos y Encuentros: Hacia una Educación Transformadora.* (2001)
  Softcover 163 pp ISBN 1-894710-08-8

A. James Reimer. *Mennonites and Classical Theology: Dogmatic Foundations for Christian Ethics.* (2001)
  Softcover, 650 pp., index. ISBN 0-9685543-7-7

Walter Klaassen. *Anabaptism: Neither Catholic nor Protestant*, 3rd ed. (2001)
  Softcover, 122 pp. ISBN 1-894710-01-0

Dale Schrag & James Juhnke, eds. *Anabaptist Visions for the new Millennium: A search for identity.* (2000)
  Softcover, 242 pp. ISBN 1-894710-00-2

Harry Loewen, ed. *Road to Freedom: Mennonites Escape the Land of Suffering.* (2001)
  Hardcover, large format, 302 pp. ISBN 0-9685543-5-0

Alan Kreider and Stuart Murray, eds. *Coming Home: Stories of Anabaptists in Britain and Ireland.* (2001)
  Softcover, 220 pp. ISBN 0-9685543-6-9

Edna Schroeder Thiessen and Angela Showalter. *A Life Displaced: A Mennonite Woman's Flight from War-Torn Poland.* (2001)
  Softcover, xii, 218 pp. ISBN 0-9685543-2-6

Stuart Murray. *Biblical Interpretation in the Anabaptist Tradition.* (2000)
  Softcover, 310 pp. ISBN 0-9685543-3-4

Loren L. Johns, ed. *Apocalypticism and Millennialism.* (2000)
  Softcover, 419 pp., indices. ISBN 0-9683462-9-4

Later Writings by Pilgram Marpeck and his Circle. Volume 1: The Exposé, A Dialogue and Marpeck's Response to Caspar Schwenckfeld. Trans. by Walter Klaassen, Werner Packull, John Rempel. (2000)
  Softcover, 157 pp. ISBN 0-9683462-6-X

John Driver. *Radical Faith. An Alternative History of the Christian Church.* Carrie Snyder, ed. (1999)
  Softcover, 334 pp. ISBN 0-9683462-8-6

C. Arnold Snyder. *From Anabaptist Seed. The Historical Core of Anabaptist-Related Identity.* (1999)
  Softcover, 53 pp., discussion questions. ISBN 0-9685543-0-X
  Also available in Spanish translation: *De Semilla Anabautista,* from Pandora Press only.

John D. Thiesen. *Mennonite and Nazi? Attitudes Among Mennonite Colonists in Latin America, 1933-1945.* (1999)
  Softcover, 330 pp., 2 maps, 24 b/w illustrations, bibliography, index. ISBN 0-9683462-5-1

Lifting the Veil, a translation of *Aus meinem Leben: Erinnerungen von J.H. Janzen.* Leonard Friesen, ed.; trans. by Walter Klaassen. (1998)
  Softcover, 128 pp., 4 pp. of illustrations. ISBN 0-9683462-1-9

Leonard Gross. *The Golden Years of the Hutterites,* rev. ed. (1998)
  Softcover, 280 pp., index. ISBN 0-9683462-3-5

William H. Brackney, ed. *The Believers Church: A Voluntary Church.* (1998)
  Softcover, viii, 237 pp., index. ISBN 0-9683462-0-0

An Annotated Hutterite Bibliography. Compiled by Maria H. Krisztinkovich; Peter C. Erb, ed. (1998)
    (Ca. 2,700 entries) 312 pp., cerlox bound, electronic, or both. ISBN (paper) 0-9698762-8-9/(disc) 0-9698762-9-7

Jacobus ten Doornkaat Koolman. *Dirk Philips. Friend and Colleague of Menno Simons.* Trans. by W. E. Keeney; C. A. Snyder, ed. (1998)
    Softcover, xviii, 236 pp., index. ISBN: 0-9698762-3-8

Sarah Dyck, ed. & trans. *The Silence Echoes: Memoirs of Trauma & Tears.* (1997)
    Softcover, xii, 236pp., 2 maps. ISBN: 0-9698762-7-0

Wes Harrison. *Andreas Ehrenpreis and Hutterite Faith and Practice.* (1997)
    Softcover, xxiv, 274 pp., 2 maps, index. ISBN 0-9698762-6-2

C. Arnold Snyder. *Anabaptist History and Theology: Revised Student Edition.* (1997)
    Softcover, xiv, 466 pp., 7 maps, 28 illustrations, index, bibliography. ISBN 0-9698762-5-4

Nancey Murphy. *Reconciling Theology and Science: A Radical Reformation Perspective.* (1997)
    Softcover, x, 103 pp., index. ISBN 0-9698762-4-6

C. Arnold Snyder and Linda A. Huebert Hecht, eds. *Profiles of Anabaptist Women: Sixteenth Century Reforming Pioneers.* (1996)
    (Waterloo, ON: Wilfrid Laurier University Press, 1996).
    Softcover, xxii, 442 pp. ISBN: 0-88920-277-X

The Limits of Perfection: A Conversation with J. Lawrence Burkholder 2nd ed., with a new epilogue by J. Lawrence Burkholder; Rodney Sawatsky and Scott Holland, eds. (1996)
    Softcover, x, 154 pp. ISBN 0-9698762-2-X

C. Arnold Snyder. *Anabaptist History and Theology: An Introduction.* (1995)
    Softcover, x, 434 pp., 6 maps, 29 illustrations, index, bibliography. ISBN 0-9698762-0-3

Pandora Press
33 Kent Avenue
Kitchener, ON
Canada N2G 3R2
Tel./Fax: (519) 578-2381
E-mail:
info@pandorapress.com
Web site:
www.pandorapress.com

Herald Press
616 Walnut Avenue
Scottdale, PA
U.S.A. 15683
Orders: (800) 245-7894
E-mail:
hp@mph.org
Web site:
www.mph.org